EXPLORER WITH A HEART:

*The Story of Giovanni da Verrazzano*

# EXPLORER
# WITH A HEART:

*The Story of Giovanni da Verrazzano*

BY

Covelle Newcomb

DAVID McKAY COMPANY, Inc.          NEW YORK

**EXPLORER WITH A HEART:**
*The Story of Giovanni da Verrazzano*

LIBRARY OF CONGRESS CATALOG CARD NUMBER: 78-81902

MANUFACTURED IN THE UNITED STATES OF AMERICA

VAN REES PRESS • NEW YORK

*Typography by Charles M. Todd*

*To*

BERTHA L. GUNTERMAN

## Acknowledgments

My appreciation and thanks to those who prefer to remain anonymous, but who know the value of their assistance and the measure of my gratitude. I owe special thanks to Professor Dr. Mario Tirelli, Rome, Italy; to Cav. Carlo Baldini, Segretario Generale, Comitato Nazionale Per Le Onoranze a Giovanni da Verrazzano, Greve in Chianti and Florence, Italy; to Priscilla Fitz-Gerald Baumann, Paris, France; to Captain George H. Evans, States Marine Isthmian Lines, New York City; to Rev. Anthony Bregolato, S.D.B., Ph.D., New York City; to Mr. Gilbert Di Lucia, Attorney, New York City; to Miss Marie R. Beaulieu, New York City; to faculty members and helpful students of Don Bosco College, Newton, New Jersey; to the librarians and pages in the American History Room, New York Public Library.

—C.N.

# AUTHOR'S NOTE

THIS IS NOT, and is not intended to be, an academic book.

Until I wrote this story-biography, I knew nothing about Giovanni da Verrazzano, except that a bridge in New York City was named in his memory. When the Verrazano-Narrows Bridge was opened, I read a number of letters-to-the-editor in various New York papers. Many correspondents found it untenable that a bridge of such cost and beauty should be named for a "pirate."

Was he a pirate? Curiosity took me to the New York Public Library. The first book about Verrazzano that I read, written by a scholarly nineteenth century American author who represented Verrazzano as "Juan Florin the French pirate," cast doubt on his voyage of 1524, and placed him in a villainous light. The author's references and his own conclusions clashed in a strange frenzy of contradictions. This spurred me to read all else that I could find about Verrazzano. I took up residence in the American History Room of the New York Public Library for the next ten months, determined to make whatever contribution I could to clearing the name of a great Italian. I also wrote for and received material from France and Italy.

Writing about Verrazzano is like tackling a huge jig-saw puzzle. The difference is that when the irregularly cut pieces of a jigsaw are fitted together they form a complete picture. The same is not the case with Verrazzano. There are bits and pieces about him in more than a hundred books. I set myself the task of trying to fit them correctly together to make a picture of the last six years of his short life.

There is a frustrating jumble of data in regard to Verrazzano's second voyage. (Some authors refer to his second voyage as his third, even fourth, depending upon which accounts one accepts as accurate.) I accept the statement that the second voyage began in June, 1526. Scarcely anyone can argue the point that it ended in 1528. A few historians believe that Verrazzano made more than one voyage to Brazil between 1526 and 1528. No log exists to prove it, although there are documents which give a measure of credence to this belief.

In order to spare the reader the confusion I experienced in reading these varying and disorganized reports, I have avoided the supposed second voyage to Brazil. If such a voyage was made by Verrazzano with a fleet of "five ships," it would have been a commercial venture. For this reason I do not feel that it is particularly important one way or the other. Verrazzano was essentially an explorer, and on his second voyage to the New World he was again intent upon finding for France a route to Asia.

As for the spelling of the name Verrazzano, Mr. Gilbert Di Lucia, Chairman of the Verrazzano Foundation, writes that for the most part Italian historians spell the name with two z's. He quotes from the 1961 edition of Treccani's *Dizionario Enciclopedico Italiano:* "Verrazzano, Giovanni da, latinzz. Janus Verrazanus di qui, in it. la rara e ingiustificata variante grafica Verrazano— Verrazzano, Giovanni da, latinized. Janus Verrazanus, from which in Italian comes the rare and unjustified written variation Verrazano."

This small book represents an effort to deliver Giovanni da Verrazzano from the obscurity which still surrounds him, to show what kind of man he was (his letter, the Cellere Codex, reveals a great deal about his character and background), and to make it clear that he was a Florentine nobleman and navigator with high, humanistic ideals, not a pirate. Nationalistic feelings, as expressed by a few non-French and non-Italian historians, have played a major part in portraying Verrazzano as an odious sea-robber, the accusations prompted all too often by what H. Harrisse calls "that narrow-minded patriotism which is the curse and the bane of historical studies."

But a bridge is not enough. Full justice and recognition yet remain to be given to the Italian explorer who can be said to have opened up to Europeans a considerable part of the North American continent. And none is more deserving of a pedestal alongside his fellow Italians, Christopher Columbus, John Cabot, and Amerigo Vespucci, than *Giovanni di Pier Andrea di Bernardo da Verrazzano, patrizio Fiorentino, Gran Capitano Comandante in Mare Per il Re Cristianissimo Francesco Primo, e Discopritore della Nuova Francia.*

—C.N.

Among the ancients it was usual to worship as gods those who discovered unknown lands. Owing to our belief in one God we may not adore the discoverers of new lands. But let us give to them our praise. We should also praise the sovereigns under whose auspices the aims of the discoverers were realized. Let us laud the one and the other, each according to his merits.

—PETER MARTYR

# CONTENTS

*Author's Note*                                    ix

PART ONE — *Dieppe—Lisbon—Seville*                  3

PART TWO — *The First Voyage*                       49

PART THREE — *The Last Voyage*                     141

*Notes*                                            217

*Bibliography*                                     233

# PART ONE

*Dieppe—Lisbon—Seville*

# 1

THE OLD French port of Dieppe, in Normandy, lay under a light glaze of spring sunshine. Today Dieppe was gay with bunting and banners, and crowded with people. *Dieppois* and visitors from neighboring ports and towns jammed the waterfront, jammed the cobbled wharf.

At the end of the quay, Jean D'Ango, Captain of Dieppe, Lieutenant of the Admiral of France, kept his gaze on a still distant galleon on her way from La Rochelle. Slowly she swayed along over blue water that quivered like acres of cornflowers rippled by the wind. Gathered round Ango were sailors, flag bearers, drummers, pipers, dignitaries, and his chosen circle of friends. Many in this circle were Italian noblemen. Some lived in Dieppe, others in Rouen and Lyons. Voluntary exiles for political reasons or because they hoped for opportunities which were not now available in Italy, all knew one another and all were members of Ango's court of intellectuals.

Now the galleon rounded the last of the chalk-white cliffs and headed for the harbor which, in the ninth

3

century, Norsemen—Normandy took her name from them—found and called "The Deep." Sailors rushed to catch the flung ropes and fix her to her moorings. The crowd yelled and cheered; a mass of voices made such a racket that only the breakers exploding against the cliffs could be heard above it.

A momentary silence held the people when, accompanied by officers of fleets he had commanded, a blond, blue-eyed Norman, square-jawed and rugged, came ashore in gold-belted crimson.

Shouts broke out anew, exultant shouts.

*"Vive la France! Vive le brave Capitaine!"*

The brave captain, Normandy's hero, was Jean Fleury of Honfleur,[1] a pirate who was wanted by John III of Portugal and Charles V of Spain. Officials in France bowed to him. Jean Ango folded him in his arms, then embraced each succeeding officer in turn. An embrace from Ango was a victor's laurels.

"Hurrah! Hurrah!"

Drums and bagpipes started up their thrilling, barbaric din.

"Move, friends, move. Step aside, please. Make way, please."

The mob divided, left a path wide enough for those clustered at the end of the pier to walk three abreast. Against the clear blue sky, the royal flag, the French Admiral Bonnivet's ensign, Jean Ango's pennon, and old Norman banners blazoned with heraldic devices, fluttered in a dazzle of colors, hoisted high and borne by proud mariners who led the march away from the wharf. Drummers and pipers followed, then the dignitaries, then Ango and his captains, and lastly Ango's special friends.

Walking along at a stately gait with two fellow Florentines, Alderotto Brunelleschi and Zanobi Rucellai, was an imposing figure of a man. Unaware that he did so, he drew attention away from Jean Fleury to himself. His austerely handsome face was as oval as the other's was squarish; his short-cropped wavy black hair as dark as Fleury's was fair; the eyes were large, bright, and black. And his elegant indigo-blue attire was as reserved as the pirate's scarlet was gaudy.

"A proud throw of the head, that one!"

"The one in blue velvet? *Eh, oui!* Who is he?"

"A Somebody, otherwise he wouldn't be in Ango's group."

Onlookers rightly believed him to be a nobleman. But never would they have believed that the man whose aristocratic bearing prodded their curiosity could ever possibly be mistaken for the pirate Jean Fleury.

Both men were born to the sea. Both had exceptional courage. Both had baptismal names which were the equivalent of the English "John." And there the likeness ended. Jean Fleury came from a long line of Norman seamen. Giovanni di Pier Andrea di Bernardo da Verrazzano, *Patrizio Fiorentino*—Florentine nobleman— was the son of Fiammetta Capelli and Ser Pier Andrea da Verrazzano of Florence and Greve in Chianti. He stemmed from a long line of wealthy bankers and importers. His family was old nobility; his crest dated back to the thirteenth century.[2] Jean Fleury of Honfleur and Giovanni da Verrazzano of Florence were two completely different individuals.[3] Yet Verrazzano, without ever knowing it, was to become a victim of mistaken identity, defamed in history as "Juan Florin the French pirate." Evidence that he was an Italian, a navigator and explorer, not a Frenchman, a pirate, or "Juan Florin," was available in print as early as 1556.[4] Even so, this distortion of the truth was one of those gross historical errors which was repeatedly proved to be an error; yet it continued to parade as the truth.

The mistake originated with Iberian pirates. Portugal's pirates turned Jean Fleury's name into Portuguese: João Florim, Florine. Spain's pirates translated his name into Spanish: Juan Florin, Florino, Florentino. Some Dieppois occasionally spoke of Giovanni da Verrazzano as *Jean le Florentin,* John the Florentine. Names all too much alike. Spanish pirates gave their form of the name to Peter Martyr. A distinguished Italian humanist, scholar, and author, Peter Martyr lived in Spain and served as court chronicler to Charles V. Master Peter wrote in Latin, so Florin became *"Florinus quidam gallus piratarum"*—Florinus, a certain French pirate. When Peter Martyr's entire *de Orbe Novo* was published in 1530, the name appeared in print for the first time.

Peter Martyr definitely referred to the French pirate Jean Fleury, although it is clear that he did not know the correct form of the name. Among later authors a number of Spanish and American historians carelessly invested Jean le Florentin, Giovanni da Verrazzano, with the piratical career, capture, and death by hanging of Juan Florin, Jean Fleury. In North America this grim misjudgment was still in print in the twentieth century.

The stares of bystanders followed Giovanni da Verrazzano. They admired, they queried. Then something else magnetized the crowd. Fleury's sailors came ashore in single file. Each carried a trophy of Fleury's most recent attack on Spanish treasure galleons from Mexico. The king of France was in Provence. Until directions were received from him regarding the precious haul, the items would be vigilantly guarded in Ango's seaside mansion.

Never before had the French seen anything of great beauty from the New World. Only codfish from Newfoundland, and from Brazil, wood, parrots, and monkeys.

But this!

"Look! Bucklers of silver studded with blue-white stones!"

"Look! Golden helmets crested with strange birds of kingfisher-green. The feet and eyes are gold!"

"*Vois, vois!* Look! Feather mantles! A long ripple of rainbow hues from neck to hem. Fastened with brooches of turquoise and powdered with chips of jade!"

"Look! Tunics of cotton as fine as silk from Eastern looms, all fringed with beads of flamelike colors!"

"Not beads, madame, fire opals."

"Ah-h, what splendor!"

"*Matelot*—sailor—is that a neckchain?"

"*Oui, monsieur.* Eight huge links set with two hundred sixty-two rubies and one hundred eighty-three emeralds. I counted them."

"Did you also count the bells at the edges of the chain?"

"Yes. There are twenty-seven golden bells and four large opals between each bell."

"Oh! Oh!"

"You, matelot, what are those things? Skulls covered with stained glass?"

"No, monsieur, mosaic masks to resemble skulls. The mosaics are gems, not glass."

"*Ciel!* Heavens! What marvels!" [5]

Minds were stunned, and not alone by exotic Aztec magnificence. With a shock, it broke in upon the people, as it already had on the king, that a world existed about which they knew nothing. And with this awareness came the stinging realization that France was excluded from it. The fault lay mainly in the papal decree of 1493. A Spanish pope who had yielded to the demands of Spain and Portugal had, in order to avoid war between the two, allowed them to grab the world. Ever since then the demon of greed had prompted the two nations to enforce marine laws that safeguarded their riches and adversely affected the economy of countries such as England, France, and Italy.

During the past three years King Francis I had openly and repeatedly denounced the papal decree as unjust and invalid. The ordinary Frenchman knew this from talking with mariners, and none knew better than these mariners that the pope of thirty years ago gave Africa and India to Portugal, and America to Spain. Denied legitimate means of trade, France, and also England, resorted to piracy for survival. For two centuries both countries had depended on Genoa and Venice to provide them with merchandise, Italian seamen being able to leave from either port and reach without hindrance the Levant, the source of many products that afforded a livelihood to French and English tradesmen. Among the numerous Italian mariners who made these regular runs to the Levant was Giovanni da Verrazzano.

Then, suddenly, in 1509, Don Manuel I of Portugal seized East Africa and the Malabar Coast, got control of the Levantine trade, banished the Italians from the Levant, secured dominion of the Indian Ocean, put Genoa and Venice out of business, and impoverished the commerce of France and England.

Portugal now policed the gates to the Levant, Africa, India, and Brazil. Spain barred her gates to the West Indies, Mexico, the Strait of Magellan and the 7000 islands (the Philippines) discovered and claimed for her by the great Portuguese navigator who defected to Spain, Ferdinand Magellan.

Now the mood of the French in Dieppe became as sullen as a stormy day.

"We'll break open their gates! They have no right to rule us, no right to stop us. We don't want their possessions, we want our own. We want more than fishing rights in a corner of the world's vast expanse of waters. Somewhere there must be a land not yet discovered. Somewhere there must be a passage that does not belong to Portugal or Spain; a sea lane to China that we can use, without danger to our lives."

"If there is such a lane, who is to find it for us?"

"Jean Fleury."

"No. Jean Fleury is a pirate, not an explorer. Besides, where would we be without the fruits of his brigandage? Dealers stand waiting to bid for the cargo he seizes. Piracy has become the lifeblood of France, and so far Fleury is her luckiest pirate."

"Who else, then?"

"There must be somebody. There has to be! Ango will give us an explorer. We'll demand it of him."

The festal spirit of the day gave place to the hot defiance of an angry equal heir who has been cast out by two arrogant brothers.

"Fight, Frenchmen, fight!"

Norman pride in Fleury took on a feverish glow. Pirate, warrior, avenger of compatriots slain by Portuguese and Spanish pirates, Fleury acquired stature as a symbol of French resistance to oppression, of French determination to win what the two Iberian nations long had monopolized and forbidden to France: freedom to explore, freedom to trade, freedom to sail the seas.

"*Vive la France! Vive le corsaire Jean Fleury!*"

They shouted on the waterfront, in the streets, in the main square. Then a great mob pressed in round Ango's house, eager for another scarlet-flashing glimpse of their hero.

"Jean Fleury! Fleury!"

"Jean d'Ango! Hear us! We want our rights. We want discoveries. Give us an explorer!"

Neither Fleury nor Ango responded to their cries. But they saw standing alone at a window the distinguished-looking gentleman in blue. Giovanni da Verrazzano regarded them with a grave smile that suggested sympathy and approval. He knew the French well enough to believe they would be relentless in their demands for equality with Spain and Portugal, and for release from the limitations which Charles V and John III forced upon them. Somehow they would get what they wanted. And so too, he hoped, would he.

While Frenchmen and others in Dieppe were celebrating the arrival of Fleury and puzzling over the identity of Giovanni da Verrazzano, in Lisbon King John III and Don Gaspar, an aged courtier who had served the king's late father, Manuel I, were arguing a matter which concerned the capture of two Portuguese vessels by a French pirate, and the capture by Portuguese pirates of a French galleon on her voyage home from Brazil with a cargo of brazilwood.[6] Don John demanded that Francis I release the Portuguese ships and crews without further ado. King Francis demanded that his galleon and Frenchmen be sent home without delay. According to the king of Portugal, the French were off limits when they sailed to Brazil to buy wood.

"They had no right to go there," said Don John to the courtier. "Men who ignore our laws must expect to pay the penalty."

"Sire, they have paid. Their cargo was confiscated, their ship impounded. The French captain and his men have been a long while in a Lisbon prison. I am an old man, sire, but I can still offer counsel. Be lenient, sire. Liberate the Normans and their vessel. Guarantee them safe-conduct to France. Friends are not made in a day, but they can be lost in an instant. Portugal does not have many friends." Don Gaspar paused, and then continued, "You mean well, sire. You issue despotic measures against non-Portuguese in order to protect Portugal's widespread possessions. Your Majesty is young, too young to realize, as yet, that in denying other nations the right to use your sea routes and to trade in Portugal's territories you force them—particularly France and England—to resort to piracy. Your restrictions, as well as those of your rival, Charles V of Spain, engender hostility."

For a moment, a royal foot tapped out indignation on the floor tiles. "I have two enemies in France," Don John said heatedly, "the king and Ango of Dieppe. Ango controls French pirates, French ports, and shipping. He orders and acts in the name of the king. Neither Francis nor Ango has honored my demands. Yet you urge me to honor theirs, to be lenient. No!"

"But sire," Don Gaspar began, then stopped.

"Look you," said the king, "I am sending Don João da Silveira to France as my new ambassador.[7] My father sent Monteiro. He is loyal but ineffectual. He and Silveira will work together. It is Silveira, however, who will get results. He's young, alert, and forceful. I can rely on him to convey to Francis my fury with that pirate of his who made off with our two vessels to La Rochelle. The same pirate attacked fleets from Mexico en route to Seville. Two sea raids occurred in our seas, in the Azores. It's nothing to me what this brigand steals from Charles V, but I will not tolerate him and his band of pirates in Portuguese waters."

Don John fell silent. Then, with a disagreeable smile, he said, "It appears that our coasts need guarding. I have an idea. My grandfather enforced this idea and rid our seas of intruders. He borrowed it from the ancient Phoenicians. They, too, had trouble with pirates. So they sank ships and crews, and soon had the Mediterranean and Aegean Seas to themselves."

The courtier closed his eyes for a second, as though to shut out the vision of the king's plan. He opened his eyes, but did not look at the king. "Sire, suppose storm winds blow a ship to our coasts?"

"Until my coast guard system is organized—it may take a year or more—all alien ships will be seized and the crews imprisoned."

Blankly, Don Gaspar stared at the cross suspended from the king's neckchain. It glittered, crusted with diamonds from Don John's African mines worked by African slaves.

Still angry, Don John said, "Ships blown off course to our coasts are less important to me at the moment than the French pirate. What is his name?"

The other did not reply. He seemed not to have heard, as he sat bent forward in his chair in an almost desolate attitude, his head lowered.

"What is his name?" repeated the king, aggressively.

"Whose name, sire?"

The king made a gesture of impatience. "The French pirate's, of course."

"Oh. Your Majesty's pirates call him João Florim and João Florine." [8]

"I want him. Advise my naval commander. Are you listening?"

"Yes, sire, I am. I will advise Don Pedro Botelho. He in turn will order all Portuguese seamen to be on watch for João Florim. Many, in fact, have tried to catch him, without success."

"They must succeed. They must capture him. I want the pirate and I want him hanged in Lisbon."

Don Gaspar smiled feebly. "I expect Charles V wants him hanged in Spain," he said. "Florim took to France considerable treasure intended for Emperor Charles. Magnificent things, I am told, sent to Charles by Hernando Cortés from Mexico."

"Charles' loss is not my concern. Mexico is rich. He owns Mexico. I want Florim. The pirates who bring him to me will be rewarded. Make it known. At once!"

"Yes, sire."

"Wait! In the event that Charles' pirates capture Florim, I authorize mine to offer a price for the Frenchman, a sum greater than the value of the diamonds in this cross," he said, and fingered the largest stone. "The equivalent in gold of this one diamond would suffice, but I am prepared to pay a mad price for João Florim."

"How much does your Majesty offer for him?"

"Ten thousand ducats in gold, and well worth it to me," he said, his voice rising, "to know that this, my triumph, will mean defeat for Charles."

At half-past three on a cloudy afternoon, Emperor Charles V was consuming the last of a twenty course dinner in the Alcázar, a Moorish-looking palace in

Moorish-looking Seville. The emperer ate gluttonously. The two Italian courtiers at table with him were nobles of advancing years and small appetite. The Marquis of Gattinara, Charles' Grand Chancellor, sat musing while he watched the play of candlefire on the barricade of wine glasses lined up in front of him. The court chronicler, Peter Martyr of Anghiera, a village on Lake Como, gazed meditatively out the open doors that led into a fountained garden of orange trees. He saw the sky darken and doves fly from the lip of the fountain basin. Master Peter wished he could fly from this chamber, from this palace, back to his house in Valladolid. He had work to do, a book to finish writing.[9]

Suddenly, Charles flicked a hand in signal.

Serving-men came forward and cleared the table of everything except fruit.

A second signal brought the major-domo. Apprised of what was wanted before the meal began, he now set before the emperor a coffer carved of oak and mounted on taloned eagles' feet. A low bow to Charles, then he, too, left the room.

"You, Master Peter, what do you know about the pirate?"

With a start, Peter Martyr looked away from the fountain to the king. At the moment, pirates were as far from his mind as from his vision.

"Sire, what pirate?"

"The French corsair who attacked my ships and took priceless cargo to Normandy for Francis I."

"I am not personally acquainted with him, sire."

"Then how does it happen that you wrote at length about him to the Pope?"

"I wrote at length about the attacks and the treasure, not about the pirate captain who commanded the raids. The Spanish flagship captain gave me an inventory of what was seized, and permitted me to see what was saved."

Charles' ice-blue eyes fastened a moment on the sixty-nine-year-old scholar and author in his rectangular hat and long, closed gown. Three decades ago this learned Italian humanist had been summoned to Spain from Italy by Queen Isabella. In the court of the late Ferdinand and Isabella, Charles' maternal grandparents, Peter Martyr had served as court historian and tutor. Abruptly, Charles raised the coffer's gabled lid and took from the box a parchment scroll, which he handed to Peter Martyr.

The author of epistles about discoverers, New World discoveries, voyages of exploration, unusual cargoes, pirates, and piracy, examined the parchment and frowned, confused.

"Do you recognize it?"

"Yes, sire. The words come back to me. They are mine. But not the handscript. I use Roman. This is German Gothic."

"So it is. What you have there is a copy of a letter you wrote to Pope Adrian VI. My German envoy to the Vatican made the copy and sent it to me, with the pope's consent. The subject matter, I believe, concerns the pirate. You write in Latin, and I am not a Latinist. Translate the letter for me."

Peter Martyr obliged the young emperor. Eventually he read these words, "During the past year, Florinus, a certain French pirate, seized a ship coming from Española with 80,000 pieces of gold, 600 pearls weighing eight ounces each, and 200 sacks of sugarcane. . . ." [10]

Master Peter scanned the remainder of the letter. "What follows," he said, "is known to your Majesty. The battle between French and Spanish pirates. I see no other mention of Florinus in this letter."

"Florinus, eh? Is that his full name?"

A clap of thunder muffled Peter Martyr's reply. He raised his voice. "Your Majesty's sailors and pirates have given me his name as Juan Florin, Juan Florino, and Juan Florentino. Juan, I assume, is his given name."

Thunder boomed. Whip-cracks of yellow lightning lashed the sky. In the garden the orange trees began to jerk and rustle. The emperor roared to Gattinara, "Enforce sterner measures against Florin, Florentino, or whatever his name is, and against all Frenchmen in Spanish waters. Post a reward for the capture of the pirate. If my pirates let him fall into Portuguese hands, they will swing from the gallows for it. I want him. For the privilege of seeing his neck in a noose, I am ready to pay handsomely. Sooner or later I shall have him, for he cruises along my coasts in spite of warnings."

"Warnings are useless in wartime, sire. You and Francis I are seldom at peace," Gattinara reminded him. "Even now you are planning to fight each other for possession of Italy. Forbidden seas? The king of France makes no secret of the fact that he regards as illegal and unjust the papal decree of 1493 which gave half the non-Christian world to Spain and half to Portugal."

"I know. And Francis insults me with a cynical letter besides. If mankind's father Adam made Spain and Portugal heirs to all the earth, he, Francis, demands to see a certified copy of Adam's will. Lacking such proof, he will allow his pirates to go wherever they please and take whatever they can." [11]

A gust of wind blew in from the patio. One candle-flame went out. Charles stared at the blackened wick. "Gold and treasure have I lost to Francis, but Francis," the emperor threatened, "will lose Italy to me as easily as this wick has lost its light. Spain will cause him another loss, Juan Florin the French pirate."

"Not immediately, sire."

"What do you mean, Master Peter?"

"Florin is safe ashore in Normandy for the time being," said Peter Martyr.

"How do you come by your information? Letters, I suppose," said Charles, answering his own question. "What more do you know about the pirate?"

"Not much more." Peter Martyr paused, rolled up the parchment and courteously returned it to the emperor. "It is rumored," he said, "that Jean d'Ango is to hold a celebration in his honor."

"Ah, yes, Ango!" said Charles, with sarcasm. "I'd almost forgotten that Florin sails under his egis. Where is this honoring, this fiesta, to take place?"

"In Dieppe."

"When?"

"Soon, I suppose."

Charles looked at him and his cold blue eyes shone with wrath. "It could already have taken place," muttered the emperor.

"Yes, sire, it could. Then again—."

"Never mind," Charles said irascibly, then took an orange from a pyramid of fruit and plunged a knife into it.

Thunder smashed over the palace. Raindrops struck the tiled garden walks like beads falling from broken chains. Out of the angry sky the wind came shrieking, and out of the mouth of an angry king came menacing words, "Florin's day of reckoning is not far off. So let him have his day in Dieppe, let him have it."

# 2

THE PARTY for Jean Fleury was over. All the guests but one had gone home. The solitary lingerer sat opposite Ango at a table in Ango's splendid library. For an hour they had engaged in talk, to no avail. Silence closed over the two friends. To each the quality of it was disturbing. In Verrazzano's ears the hush was loud with the sound of dashed hopes, falling like rock on rock. He was, for the moment, crestfallen.

"Giovanni, I am sorry."

"So am I. Very sorry." Verazzano let his gaze wander over the valuable books displayed on carved lecterns and glass-topped tables with marble bases.

"Handsome," he said. "The late lord of Florence, Lorenzo the Magnificent, would be flattered could he know that a gentleman of your tastes and learning is referred to in Normandy as the 'Lorenzo de' Medici of Dieppe.'" Slowly Verrazzano looked from Ango's books to his paintings, sculptures, and tapestries in a way a man looks for the last time at things that have given him pleasure. Reminded of libraries in the palaces of eminent familes of Florence, Ango's library, Florence, and rural Tuscany merged in Verrazzano's mind. Briefly he closed his eyes.

"I shall remember this room just as I remember Florence and my villa and garden near Florence, at Greve in Chianti." Homesick, he said softly, "I love Greve. The hills, the vineyards, the meadows of wild irises; my garden, my cypress trees."

"Why do you say that? I mean about my library. It is at your disposal. You are welcome here at any time."

Verrazzano did not answer.

The sun was going under, the great room growing dark. Ango rang a hand bell.

An elderly servant appeared.

"Bring lights, Pierre."

"At once, monsieur." Pierre paused, looked at Verrazzano, one of his favorites among Ango's many friends. Odd, no smile, no greeting. Verrazzano merely stared at him vacantly. Pierre disappeared, then reappeared bringing two ornate candelabra. Tapers flowered from the gilt bronze branches in rosy-orange flame that shone upon the polished ebony table. For a second, Pierre stood stock-still, eyes on Verrazzano who felt his inquiring look and was wishing he would go.

"Shall I bring wine, monsieur?"

"Yes, please," Ango said, as if he, too, hoped that wine might help.

Pierre soon returned and with great fuss set before Ango a tray with goblets of thin Venetian glass and a crystal wine decanter. The moment Pierre left the room Verrazzano got to his feet.

Surprised, Ango said, "You are not leaving?"

"Yes."

"But why?"

"Why stay, monsieur?" Verrazzano smiled dimly. "I have a goal, but my country has no king. Italian explorers are forced to go outside their own country to seek royal sponsorship for voyages of discovery and exploration. Columbus and Vespucci went to Spain. John Cabot chose England." Verrazzano watched the flames that darted from the candle tips. Resignedly he said, "Their appeals met with more success than mine."

Another unsettling silence came between them.

Although his face was almost expressionless, Verrazzano's purpose, unalterable as fate, shone in his eyes. Gazing squarely at Ango, he relieved the silence.

"Monsieur, it isn't clear to me why you turned down my proposition. Perhaps you feel that if it is to be tried a Frenchman should be the one to try it. I can understand that. But if you imagine it is personal gain and glory that I want, you could not be more mistaken. Money I do not need, and what would I do with glory? Whether I achieve anything or not, I will be forgotten. That is as certain as that light comes and goes with the sun. It doesn't matter. No Italian navigator has ever sailed under a foreign flag for the glory of it. Columbus was filled with a mystical sense of mission. Vespucci explored with the motives of a geographer and scientist. Giovanni Caboto sailed in a spirt of high adventure and with the objectives of a merchant. What motivates me? I don't think I really knew until today. Now all that matters to me is to find a northwest passage to the Orient, for France I had hoped, and I hoped that indirectly it would benefit Italy also. A voyage such as I have in mind would bring new knowledge to me and to those who come after."

He stood mute and motionless. Candlefire quivered upon the severe face, set agleam the silk-embroidered lilies on the velvet doublet and the seven crystal buttons down the front. He seemed all color and movement, but he was somber and still as a stone.

"Giovanni, you've been in Dieppe for some time now, and not until an hour ago did you confide this desire to find a passage to the Orient. This I find strange."

"I was waiting for an auspicious occasion to broach the matter to the king or to you. Today seemed to be the day."

"I wish you'd sit down, Giovanni."

"Thank you, no."

"As you please. Why today?"

"Because, monsieur, today the people were aroused to the injustices they endure at the hands of Portugal and Spain. I was a long while at the window. I heard the mob. I visited the room where the Aztec treasure is on view. There I heard the nobles. The one shouted, the other was low-spoken, but the outrage was the same. Seeing the precious things opened the eyes of Frenchmen in every walk of life and set them thinking. As never before, they realized that France is in bondage. Tied down. Restricted. Portugal and Spain deny French traders the use of their seaways to the East. They deny France the right to explore, to find and colonize shores beyond her own, while they, between them, own most of the world and enjoy the freedom of the oceans."

"It never occurred to me," Ango said, with increasing astonishment, "that you were analyzing the warlike mood of the mob and silently applauding it." Ango took from the table a paper knife knobbed with a ruby the color of the unpoured wine and fingered the glinting blade. Grimly curious, he asked, "Why do you, a Florentine nobleman, feel so intensely about the French, specifically the common folk?"

"Being a Florentine of good birth has nothing to do with it. I would feel similarly about any people anywhere who are subdued by nations mightier than their own, people born with rights they cannot exercise, and nobody to help them."

"In short, you are your brother's keeper."

"I hadn't thought of it that way."

"When you come right down to it," Ango said, "that is the core of humanism. Not many of us are genuinely humanistic, as you are. You're a paradox. A solitary by nature, yet a man with a heart for all mankind. And you typify the humanist's despisal of injustice. Giovanni, you give me food for thought."

"Never mind me. The needs of your people are what you ought to be thinking about. Fleury's cargo created an upheaval. Make a man think, you inspire him to act. What happened in Dieppe is certain to occur elsewhere in France. Resentment can lead to violence and violence to open revolt. Unless," he added, "somebody discovers a trade route for France, discovers lands that she can claim and settle, and makes her independent. Jean Fleury turned the tide, so to speak. It was my hope to go out on this tide. The king is unavailable, so I put my plan to you, the king's factor. But," he ended on a long sigh, "you are not for it."

Ango scowled at the paper knife. "Giovanni, what happens now?"

"I'm not sure." He paused. "I ought to be leaving," he said, and continued to stand where he was. Regal and handsome, he might have been a young Florentine noble that Verrocchio had hewn from marble.

But he wasn't marble. Ango saw burning disappointment beneath the icy composure.

"Staying in France?"

"No, monsieur. Where would it get me? Nowhere."

"Returning to Italy?"

"Not yet. Not until I have accomplished something that will do honor to my homeland."

"Well then what? Portugal?"

"No. John II ordered all Genoese and other Italians out of Portugal. Manuel I outlawed us from the Levant. John III is reducing Italy, France, and England to a state of vassalage. The same is true of Spain, except that she hasn't banished Italians. Avarice motivates both kings. The people are not to blame. I do not accuse the people, only their kings." His face became thoughtful, remote. "I could not in conscience serve a king whose forebears ran out my people and who continues to enforce their policies. I might try England."

The quietly spoken words had the effect of a slap across Jean Ango's face. "England? Did you say England?"

"Why not England? Henry VII accepted John Cabot. Henry VIII might take me on."

"Don't count on it. Two years ago he turned down the son of John Cabot, in spite of Cardinal Wolsey's urgings that he let Sebastian Cabot explore for England."

Verrazzano smiled. "What you say indicates that England is considering an explorer to find a trade lane for her to the Orient. Trade-wise, she is no better off than France and Italy. When John II seized control of the Guinea Coast for Portugal, he forbade England to trade with Guinea and intercepted her ships. Ever since then, England has been clamped down by Portugal. Spain has not shown leniency either. In two years a lot can happen to change a king's outlook."

"And if it hasn't?"

"I'll wait. One day my chance will come."

Bluntly, Ango said, "France or England, it is one and the same to you?"

"It wasn't one and the same to me. Now—" His black eyes brooded, yet glowed with resolve. "I regret having to put it this way to you, monsieur, but nothing that you can say or do will weaken my purpose."

"Giovanni."

"Yes?"

"I turned you down because the trouble with France is no money. Ocean-going expeditions are costly."

"I know that. Look, let us drop this day into the wastebasket. Forget the whole thing. And remember only our mutual regard for one another. By your leave, I must go now."

"No!" In his agitation, Ango let the knife fall to the floor.

In two strides Verrazzano was at his side, picked it

up and placed it on the table. "Careful, monsieur, that's a ruby, not a blob of glass."

"Eh, *Seigneur!* By your leave, I must go now." Ango mimicked Giovanni's formal style of speech. "About to walk out on me, without a word. Sit down, Giovanni!"

He sat. He smiled at this rough-hewn Norman for whom he felt deep affection.

"I believe you told me that your banker-brother in Rome has pledged financial assistance in the event that you find a patron to authorize this voyage."

"That is correct. Bernardo will contribute, and I am prepared to pay my share."

"Well now, there are Florentine bankers and merchants in Dieppe, Rouen, and Lyons—compatriots of yours and friends of us both—who can be relied upon to contribute to this venture. Albizzi, Gondi, Buonacorsi, Sartini, Guadagne, Toscanelli, Colardi, and others.[1] A voyage of this magnitude requires the king's blessing. Assured that the funds can be obtained from sources other than the treasury, King Francis will bestow his blessing freely."

"And if I find a passage to the sea that flows to China, imagine the problems it will solve for France!"

"I've thought of that. And you had better think of the difficulties you are apt to encounter. Forty years ago Vasco da Gama had orders to seize every French vessel in sight. The directive still holds. At sea we are chased by the Portuguese, at home we are plagued by John's envoys. Even now, Monteiro and Silveira are howling for restitution of the cargo taken from the caravel and galleon that we sent back to Lisbon. Monteiro claims that we falsify records, force admissions out of captured Portuguese pirates, twist whatever they say to suit ourselves. According to him, 'from the Admiral down to the least official,' we have but one object, to lie and deceive.[2] Before you are out of harm's way, you will have to skirt coasts that belong either to Portugal or Spain."

"I'm aware of that. I have faith—"

Verrazzano was cut short by Ango who said, "No man ever undertook a hazardous adventure without faith. All the same, faith or no faith, if you are seen you will be caught."

"In the worst situation, monsieur, there is always hope."

"More idealistic talk! Giovanni, there's pirate in me but not in you. Believe me, idealism is no help in confronting enemy pirates. For that you need a cold heart and a sharp sword."

"I can use a sword if I have to. However, I don't intend to be captured."

"With care, maybe you won't be. Care and secrecy. Portugal and Spain must not get wind of this voyage. Every detail is to be guarded with the utmost secrecy." Ango laced his strong fingers together and studied Verrazzano with a touch of anxiety. Then he said, "Yours will be the first voyage of exploration ever officially authorized by a king of France. But you go at your own peril."

"That doesn't worry me. There are ways to escape peril."

"Well I hope there are. *Voilà!* I'll get word to the

king and Admiral Bonnivet, and have a contract drawn up for you. In the meantime you map out what you believe to be the safest route. We'll go over it together. Leave the rest to me. Oh, yes, if you like, I will offer Brunelleschi the captaincy of a vessel in your fleet."

Verrazzano beamed. "I'd like that very much, monsieur. How many vessels will I have?"

"Four, probably."

"Any idea when I can sail?"

"Barring some unforeseen delay, you ought to be able to embark in June."

"From Dieppe?"

"Probably. But keep it to yourself. Don't even say it to your shadow. Portuguese and Spanish spies are planted everywhere in France, especially in the ports." Suddenly he remembered the wine. *"Barbebleu!* We must drink to your voyage." He poured wine into the clear goblets, served Verrazzano, then raised his glass and said, "To secrecy and a safe voyage!"

Presently the two men stood. A robust man, Ango placed his big rock-hard hand on Verrazzano's shoulder and smiled. In turn, Verrazzano thanked him for everything with a stateliness that was second nature to him.

Restless after he left Ango's house, Verrazzano wandered about the quiet streets. The bells of St. Jacques clanged the hour, the quarter and the half-hour. Bell tones floated above steep-slanted roofs with chimneys and gables. He halted and listened. Then he walked to the end of the quay.

Norman fishermen were just setting out in their small boats. Brave men. Brave little boats. The year round, men and boats defied pirates, the ocean, and the wet, bone-chilling fogs of Newfoundland. The boats' lanterns glowed and made undulating, saffron-colored paths across the water.

Verrazzano waved and wished them well.

He looked straight ahead at the bastion of cliffs, blue-white in the moonlight, and strong against the crashing waves. In his mind's eye he followed the coastline down to the broad estuary of the Seine. He imagined he was walking the deck of a carrack, his step as buoyant as the sails that were taking him—but where? He knew and yet he didn't know. For what explorer could be sure where he was going when he set a course in search of a passage which had been sought by many and none had found?

However, not long after, somebody else knew or thought he knew where Verrazzano was going. In the village of Poissy, famed as the home of St. Louis of France, who always signed himself *Louis de Poissy*, João da Silveira was signing a letter to the king of Portugal. He alerted John III to the fact that the French were organizing an expedition, its destination was *"Cathayo"*—Cathay—its commander *"João Verazano."* [3]

# 3

AUTUMN was nearly over. The wind was raw, the sea stone-gray. Hugging his mantle about him, Verrazzano sat alone on a boulder on a rock-strewn shore in Brittany. He stared at the fanged reefs that rose like black, odd-shaped islands in the dull glimmer of the water, but what he was actually seeing was a memory: a galloping gale, and two of his four ships vanishing beneath the surface of a wrathful sea.

Exactly where his ships sank is not known. But in the report which he was to write about the voyage, Verrazzano offered a clue as to where the misfortune occurred. He was sailing, he wrote, "toward the north, passing 66 degrees latitude, continuing along the coast and returning toward the east and arriving at 70 degrees latitude." He mentions Norway as being situated at 71 degrees latitude. It is believed, therefore, that Verrazzano might have reached the northern extremity of Norway [1] and that it was there the storm crashed down on his fleet of four ships, demolished two vessels, and forced him to return with the crippled *Normande* and the *Dauphine*, putting in at an unnamed port in

Brittany.[2] Whatever port it was, it had a shipyard capable of rebuilding ocean-going vessels.

Verrazzano's latitudes, and his comment on Norway, lend support to the view that he hoped to get to Cathay—China—by a northern route. Perhaps he meant to take a northeasterly direction to Norway, then on to Russia and from Russia to China. Or perhaps he intended to sail from Norway or Russia to America and there seek a northwest passage to the Orient. Rather than cross the paths of Portuguese and Spanish pirates, he might well have chosen one or the other of these roundabout ways.

When he set forth again, however, he would have to accept the likelihood of attack by Iberian pirates. A second attempt to cover the furiously stormy northern track was out of the question. And if he had no reason to feel full of triumph, he did not feel either that he had reason to despair. No lives were lost in the storm, he still had two carracks, and even though he noticed unfriendliness toward himself on the part of numerous sailors, having Brunelleschi with him made up for it all. For Verrazzano, who loved Italy intensely, the presence of his compatriot represented a link with home.

Moist winds wafted to Verrazzano the acrid smell of boiling pitch and the sound of hammers pounding on the hulls of his two ships. He sprang off the boulder, and as he walked along the rocky shore toward the shipyard his heart beat in time with the booming of the hammers. Halfway there, he saw Brunelleschi outside the shipyard gates, his peacock-green hat plume shivering in the wind. A noisy crowd of sailors surrounded him, flailing the air with their arms, turning thumbs downward, shouting and arguing all at the same time, while he stood first upon one foot and then the other, and seemed to make no effort to speak or to quiet them.

Clearly, trouble of some kind was brewing. His step strong and determined, his bearing unusually assertive, Verrazzano strode to the gates.

Brunelleschi was not aware, for a moment, that Verrazzano was behind him. He flushed when he saw him, and thundered for silence.

"No! Let them shout," said Verrazzano. "It is better so."

"Why?"

"Why not? Have you forgotten the old battle cry of Florence? *Popolo e libertà.* The people and liberty. These are free men, at liberty to express themselves. They evidently have complaints. It is their right to air them and my right to know what they are."

"*Va bene,*" Brunelleschi said with a shrug, then edged a little away from him.

All saw the commander now. He stood before them, self-possessed and indomitable. A handsome man of imperious mien, Verrazzano had a pure Tuscan face, oval, clear-featured, dark-eyed, and steep-browed. He was dressed in golden-brown velvet. His Italian cloak had a high-standing collar and flowed regally from his straight shoulders. He looked from man to man, then he said, "Clamor has changed to quiet. You are silent. Why?"

No one replied.

"What are your grievances?"

No one replied.

Verrazzano wished to be fair. He urged them to be open with him.

Sullen, they huddled in groups and said nothing.

"At sea," Verrazzano said, "some among you resented the discipline I demanded. Here you resent monotony. This place palls on you. You haven't enough to do, and no place to go except the tavern. I understand all that. I, too, am restless and eager to leave. Nevertheless, having survived a storm such as we came through, it is a pity that you cannot be thankful for the sunshine when the rain is gone. You go about as with a sense of loss. The goal remains. Cathay remains. The sea has not dried up. Apart from time, what has been lost?"

No one replied.

"I appear to be the cause of your discontent. What is it that you hold against me? Speak. I want the truth."

Again no one replied.

Verrazzano hated evasion. He roared out in French. *"Répondez-moi!"*

Very well, they thought, he asked for it, let him have it.

"You're a nobleman, not a navigator!"

"You're haughty and domineering!"

"You are Italian. We are French. Why should we take orders from an alien?"

Livid with rage, a French officer made a lunge for the man who shouted this bias, but he was held back by Verrazzano's quick and powerful hand.

"You would endanger our lives again. What for? For a mad obsession. You'll never find Cathay, never!"

The barbed words stung, then broke and fell away

from Verrazzano's mind the way raindrops broke when
they hit the jagged Breton reefs and trickled off into
the sea.

"Is there more?" asked Verrazzano.

"Yes! Jean d'Ango made you famous. He influenced
the admiral and the king in your favor. Jean d'Ango is
more to blame than anybody else."

Scorn burned in Verrazzano's eyes for the man who
spoke against Ango, to whom they all owed their
livelihoods.

Not all the roughnecks shared the ungrateful one's
attitude. Ango's defenders dealt blows to the chins of
his critics, and here and there a sailor lifted another
off his feet, shook him, then threw him to the ground.

Verrazzano looked on. If a Frenchman chose to in-
tervene, well and good. He, an alien, would not. For
knowing the reply that many would make to the question he was yet to ask, he did not feel it was his place
to order these men to do one thing or the other. If any
men at all from the original four crews were of a mind
to sail with him, the number would be few, too few
to need two ships. He would send the malcontents back
to Dieppe in one of the two.

Presently peace was restored.

Verrazzano said, "One final question. What were you
demanding of Captain Brunelleschi?"

"Home!" went up the cry. "We demanded to go
home."

It was the answer Verrazzano anticipated. Calmly he
said,

"So be it. As Expedition Commander of his Most

Christian Majesty, Francis I, I am committed to the service of France. I intend to continue with the voyage as soon as possible. It is my duty and my privilege. Work on the *Normande* is nearing completion. The *Normande* will take you home." He paused. Then, with no show of hard feelings, he said, "Since you are no longer members of the expedition, you are no longer subject to my orders. The matter is closed."

Silence lay over the men, the silence of shame. Some reddened. Some kicked stones with the toes of their wooden sabots. Grudging respect showed in the eyes of a few, and not a few felt contemptuous of themselves. They knew better. And yet... Aimlessly they wandered off to the village tavern.

Verrazzano watched them go, and was glad that it was over.

"*Monsieur le commandant,* we regret this demonstration."

Verrazzano looked round, found himself face to face with a distinguished naval expert, Antoine de Conflans. Older than Verrazzano, he was renowned as the author of two widely read treatises, one on navigation, the other on marine warfare.[3] Gathered around Conflans were forty-nine mariners.

"Thank you, monsieur, but you need not apologize. I asked for the truth."

"You did not ask for insults."

"No. However, I expected something of the kind. Many of the men have avoided me ever since we came to Brittany. If they met me by accident they glared at me resentfully. At first I supposed their bad humor was due to boredom. Later I sensed there was more to it than being confined to this port." Verrazzano stopped, looked at Conflans, an unasked question in his eyes.

Conflans asked and answered it for him. "Why have fifty of us stayed behind? Because, monsieur, we value your navigational skill and we understand the value of a disciplined crew. Your skill and your strictness saved our lives in that fearful storm. We trust you, *mon commandant,* and hope you will trust us too."

Verrazzano had met with so little friendliness of late that he was confused. "I am not sure that I know what you mean, monsieur."

"This: we are of one mind to make the voyage with you."

For a moment Verrazzano faltered, shaken with emotion. Quickly he mastered himself, and glanced from the famed Conflans to the least deck hand. The mouth that could be so stern could also flash an engaging smile.

"*Mes amis,* you do France a great service and me a great honor. I am grateful. Very grateful." His face alight with happiness, he turned, thinking to see Brunelleschi nearby. But his friend was not there. "Where," he asked, "is Captain Brunelleschi?"

A very young blond, blue-eyed Norman sailor, who once had been somewhat intimidated by Verrazzano's stern aspect and noble birth only to find that he needn't be, came forward, ready to search the island for the commander's friend. He was all of a sudden boyishly delighted.

"I see him!"

"Do you?"

"Yes, mon commandant. There, near the path that goes to the village. Shall I fetch him, monsieur?"

"Please, Matelot." Consciously or not, Verrazzano had always singled out this devoted boy by calling him Matelot, Sailor, as though it were his given name.

After a short wait Brunelleschi returned, and the sailor joined his companions, all of whom moved off to one side so that the two friends could be alone together.

Verrazzano's probing black eyes were fixed inquiringly on Brunelleschi, who turned crimson and then paled. A wordless moment stretched between them.

"What is wrong?" Verrazzano said.

Brunelleschi exhaled his breath in a deep sigh. "I don't know what to say to you, Giovanni."

"Just say whatever it is. Can't you?"

"Not easily."

"Oh. You are not going with me. Is that it?"

Brunelleschi nodded. "I have lost my nerve," he said.

"You owe it to yourself to do as you think best. I would be the last one to urge you to go if that is how you feel."

"I know that, Giovanni. And you ought to be the first to rebuke me."

"No reason to. Besides, we are friends. Besides that, you are not driven as I am by what the men called a 'mad obsession.'" He studied the other thoughtfully. "Please," he said, "don't torment yourself for nothing."

Brunelleschi said quietly, "I do not have your courage or your heart. You so fervently hope to help a nation throw off the chains that other powers hold it in that you are prepared, if need be, to die in the attempt. You have the explorer's zeal, but what makes you different from the others is that your zeal is governed by your heart and your humanistic ideals. Fleury's day in Dieppe gave you a motive to press for this opportunity, and of such depth is this motivation that it conquers and transcends fear. For that, Giovanni, I envy you."

Verrazzano was silent.

The wind hummed. From the fifty mariners came a low drone of talk. Waves splashed on reefs as dark as the black crucifix veiled in mist atop a stony crag above the sea. Now and again a curlew flapped its brown wings and cried.

"Giovanni."

"Yes."

"About the men who backed out, not all are against you. Only a few. What every one of them is really against is his own cowardice. Never before were they tested in such a drastic way as in those northern waters. The storm robbed them of valor and spirit, as it also robbed me. The dream of Cathay shattered before them like the sea's spray when they saw two ships go down. Now they are unwilling to sail toward Portugal's Madeiras, the route you plan to take. They see themselves being captured by Portuguese pirates and sentenced for life to hard labor in one or the other of Portugal's two African penal colonies. Ceuta in North Africa or São Tiago in West Africa, either one would be hell on earth. It dismays me to realize that my dread of this possibility is not less than theirs. I, too, was ashamed to admit to being afraid. I tried to get away from you.

Even the rudest Normans are proud, Giovanni. Sooner than reveal to you feelings that disgrace them, they made you the scapegoat of complaints which, on the whole, are limited to a very few."

Staring at the granite-gray sea, Verrazzano said, "No one is immune to fear; no one can dispute its power."

"Giovanni, my word on it, the men who are going home will not come in contact with the brave ones who are remaining with you. I will see to that. When we debark in Dieppe nobody except Ango will be told when you expect to sail and which route you intend to follow. The men won't talk. They are French. Most of the fifty who are going with you are French. Regardless of what the ruffians said to you, they know that you are making the voyage for the good of France. They will welcome any chance to redeem themselves, and in some measure they can by keeping everything about this voyage in absolute confidence. They will, for they know there must be no slips, no telling anybody anything. Spies can split their throats asking questions; they'll get no answers other than that we encountered a devastating storm. Four ships left Dieppe in June. One returned. Portuguese and Spanish spies will doubtless assume that three vessels sank, and you with them."

A smile came into Verrazzano's eyes, a smile that showed above all a gleam of bright hope. "Let that notion take root in their minds," he said, "and you will render us an immense favor. It may not, but it could mean the difference between escape and capture."

"I'll do my best," Brunelleschi promised. "And now

it's time I was off. I'm going to the tavern and issue orders to the men."

"*Buona fortuna!*" Verrazzano called to him, wishing
him good luck.

Now the fifty mariners came forward.

Conflans said, "Is Brunelleschi sailing with you?"

"No, monsieur, but in his own way he will serve us.
Later I will explain." Verrazzano looked at his men.
They waited.

"Gentlemen," he said finally, "what I have to say will
not take long, but I urge you to give heed to it. When
we leave Brittany our course will take us uncomfort-
ably close to Portugal's Madeira Islands. Danger prowls
those waters. Unlike myself, most of you are married
and have children. Consider them as well as yourselves
in arriving at a decision. You are free to change your
minds. There is no scandal in it if you do. All I ask is
that you say so without fear and without delay, for once
the *Normande* has left, and she is leaving soon, it will
be too late."

The men merely stood and smiled, and then Conflans, the eldest, spoke to the youngest, the sailor who
had brought Brunelleschi back to Verrazzano. After a
brief hush he stepped up and replied for them all.

"Mon commandant, we are resolved to make the voyage with you. Our decision is unalterable."

More touched than surprised, Verrazzano fought a
thickness in his throat, and then he thanked them once
again.

An officer said, "Is it too soon to ask how long before
the *Dauphine* can put to sea?"

Verrazzano smiled. "Offhand, I'd say six to eight weeks. That's only a guess, mind you."

It was a good guess. Two months went by. Autumn was gone and the *Normande* too. The wailing winds of winter had come. Conflans, appointed captain by Verrazzano, inspected the *Dauphine* and declared her seaworthy.

Sturdily built, the three-masted carrack of about 120 tons [4] was fortified with guns and carried provisions for eight months. Nearly everything about her now was new except her name, which in French has two meanings: prince and dolphin. She had been named for the little crown prince or *dauphin* Francis, son of King Francis I and Queen Claude. Ships generally took the feminine form of a name, thus *Dauphine*. An ancient armorial device of the *dauphins* of France was a dolphin. The galleon's figurehead was a dolphin with a beaklike snout. Ably carved, it was some eight feet in length and was painted emerald with touches of rose, violet, and gold. In varying lights the colors changed, just as the colors of live dolphins brighten and change when the fish are taken out of water.

At twilight of a wintry day, a prolonged trumpet call stabbed the cold air and signaled the *Dauphine's* departure. From her mainmast flew the royal flag of France; on the mast above the crow's nest rippled a flag with a crimson cross, the flag of Florence, home of Giovanni da Verrazzano, commander of the first French expedition ever sent out under royal auspices. Shipyard workers, sailors, fishermen, and a handful of other Bretons watched from the shore as, with lanterns lit and cressets flaming, the high-pooped white carrack, a light vessel with a long stern, slipped away into the oncoming darkness of a gusty night.

On the seventeenth day of January, 1524, the *Dauphine* carefully approached a rocky atoll southeast of the Madeiras. Uninhabited, bare even of shrubs, Verrazzano referred to the small island as a "deserted rock." An hour or so before sundown he anchored at the rock. There wasn't a ship in sight, but Verrazzano took nothing for granted. He ordered sails furled, and as little activity as possible.

Awaiting nightfall, tension mounted. All knew that a Portuguese vessel could suddenly appear. All eyes were nailed to the horizon. In the silence, sounds were magnified. The water that gently sloshed against the *Dauphine's* sides seemed as loud as pounding combers. A sea bird's rattling cry froze the blood of every man on board. Then—quiet, deep quiet. Everywhere quiet. The men looked at one another uneasily, and tried to smile away the strange state to which repressed anxiety had brought them. The only smile that lifted some of this weight was Verrazzano's. His composure gave strength and confidence, the steady black eyes that expressed pride in his crew encouraged and said for him, Hold on. It won't be much longer.

At last, the sun began to lower. One side of the rock lay in shadow. Sunset tints faded into dusk. Grape-blue dusk darkened into night.

Verrazzano spoke in whispers.

"No lights," he said to the bosun.

"Right, monsieur."

"Man the guns."

"Yes, monsieur."

"Are the men all darkly clothed?"

"All, monsieur."

"Good."

Night deepened. The wind rose. Bits of pale clouds drifted overhead.

In Conflan's cabin on the quarterdeck, Verrazzano gave the ship's captain an anxious look. Almost inaudibly he said, "Now, *mon capitaine?*"

"Yes."

Verrazzano left the cabin and gave sailing orders.

In the faint radiance of a mist-haloed moon, sailors in dark brown breeches and hooded black canvas smocks hurried to the mastheads and spread out on the yards.

"Cat the anchors."

With as little noise as possible, sailors hoisted the bow anchors and fastened them to the cathead, a projecting beam near the bow.

"Set the sails."

Yardsmen loosed the brails, the big sails swooped downward, then lifted, catching the wind.

Slowly the *Dauphine* eased away from the rock. Slowly she turned westward, and the hearts of the men turned too.

Minutes passed. Verrazzano gripped the rail of the poopdeck and stood very still. He looked and listened, his dark large eyes fixed on the "deserted rock" until he could see it no more. He did not move. He stayed at the rail of the stern deck which had no roof but the sky. The strain he was under made him alternately icy-cold, and then hot. At last his forced steadiness crumbled and he quivered.

"Lord, Lord," he begged, his face uplifted, "free us from this terror. Take us out of danger, into the empty ocean. Lord, grant..." He was too spent to think of anything more to say.

He could not have said how long he'd been standing there. Maybe half an hour, he wasn't sure. But suddenly he was joyously sure of the surging pulsations of the ocean, of the deck dipping and rising with the sea's motion. The poop's lantern, he noticed, had been lit. This meant they were well out of harm's way. Limp with relief, he murmured a fervent *Grazie a Dio!* Thanks be to God.

Somebody other than the helmsman was behind him. The young sailor of the vivid blue eyes and boundless loyalty was softly intoning a sailor's little hymn to Mary, Star of the Sea:

> *Astre propice aux marins,*
> *Conduit ma barque au rivage.*
> *Preserve-moi du naufrage,*
> *Blanche Étoile du matin.*

> O sailor's watchful Star
> Guide my ship to shore.
> Preserve me from shipwreck,
> O White Morning Star.

The commander's lips moved. He repeated the words, though not aloud.

When the sailor finished his sung petition and praise, he said with simplicity, "Mon commandant, you made us all brave. We shall never doubt your courage or your goal. It was a misty moon we saw in the Madeiras, but what a sunrise we shall see in Cathay!"

"Yes, Matelot," Verrazzano said, a slight catch in his voice, "what a sunrise we shall see in Cathay!"

# PART TWO
## *The First Voyage*

# 4

For Giovanni da Verrazzano the year 1524 was to be a year of memorable experiences and dates. It began for him with the hushed night-departure, *January 17*,[1] from the "deserted rock." After this night of shared uncertainty and risk, the hands of all on the *Dauphine* were more than ever firmly joined. Mutual confidence and respect marked the attitude of Verrazzano and his prize crew of volunteers. Every man of the fifty was loyally allied with him in his aim to find a northwest passage to the South Sea—the Pacific—sail across it to Asia, and thus establish for France a trade route to the riches of the East. These men understood Verrazzano. Severity, they realized, was as natural to him as the benevolence it concealed, even as his armor concealed Tuscan velvet beneath its steel.

On his part, Verrazzano dealt courteously with all his men. Whether he needed to or not, he respected his officers to the extent of soliciting their advice. Impartial, he showed no favoritism, but in his heart he felt for Conflans and the young sailors a real, if hidden, affection.

Congenial men and congenial wintry weather made for a smoothness that equalled the *Dauphine's* as she glided along on an even keel, her motion as steady as the *"subsolano"*—Verrazzano called the winds by their classical names [2]—that blew, he wrote, *"con dolce e suave lenità,"* [3] with sweet and gentle lenity. By day the water was brilliantly blue; by night a Sahara of ocean mirrored a skyful of stars and shimmered with the moon's luster.

*February 10.* Verrazzano, who kept the reckoning and calculated the daily positions on the chart, announced their headway. Since their departure from the rock, the east-south-east subsolano had swept them 800 leagues westward. Marine leagues varied from country to country and time to time. The nautical measure of distance used by Verrazzano was the Italian or Roman league, one league being equivalent to four miles. So, from nightfall of January 17 to midday of February 10, the *Dauphine* had logged a record 3,200 miles of Atlantic.

If sailing were only always as easy as that! If a mariner had always good seas, good winds, the sun all day and the stars all night, he would gladly ride the waves for the rest of his life! But that is not the way of the sea, or of the land either.

*February 24.* Early morning was cold and bleak and almost windless. The *Dauphine* barely moved on the gray-agate sea. No wind, no sound except the sound of stillness, intensified by the wing beat and mewing of stormy petrels, small sea birds, so named in allusion to the tradition that St. Peter had lightly walked the sea. Petrels seldom settled on it; they merely skimmed the

surface. Many a sailor regarded petrels as a sign of ill
omen. When, suddenly, a myriad of petrels fluttered
crazily back and forth across the *Dauphine's* spars,
more than one of her sailors held his breath.

Somewhere, too, the wind was holding its breath.

Eastward, awesome thunderheads began to roll up
out of the horizon. Verrazzano studied them intently
from the poop. Higher and higher the great bulks of
plum-black cloud drew up into the grayish pallor, while
distant lightning flashed along the lower horizon rim.
He had no way of knowing whether the impending
storm was a squall or a gale, or when it would strike.
But he knew the *Dauphine* could not escape. She hadn't
a chance to run before it. Would it, he wondered, be
anything like the Levanter, the tempestuous wind that
howled over the Mediterranean Sea from the east and
churned its azure into a thrashing white fury?

Unfamiliar with the Atlantic's moods, he knew the
Mediterranean's well, having learned navigation in its
waters. For ten or more years he commanded merchant-
men which he sailed to the Levant, where he loaded on
cargo to take back to Italy. He knew the principal
ports of Egypt, Syria, Lebanon, and Turkey [4] as well as
he knew Florence, Genoa, and Rome. His voyaging
came to an end in 1509, when Manuel I of Portugal
drove resident Italians out of the Levant and closed
Levantine ports to Italian traders and mariners.

Now from afar came a sound that reminded him of
the groaning of an old camel. Petrels soared and flew
away, looking like bits of charred paper tossed high into
space. Clouds were massing together and moving for-

ward, driven by the wind. Nearer and nearer they came, until the plum-black congestion overspread the lowering sky. Daytime shrank into nightlike darkness. The ocean lay languorous as the Nile, until now. Now it moved a little and became heavier, like a milky gruel thickening at a slow boil. The camel-groaning changed into sharp, booming reverberations. And suddenly the sea was heaving. The tremor of it sent a warning from Verrazzano's feet to his brain.

In turn, Verrazzano hastened to warn Captain Conflans.

"Monsieur, we are in for a blow. A hard one, if I know anything about winds." He looked at the older man, hesitated a moment, and spoke with his usual respect but in a voice tinged with severity, implying that he meant what he was saying.

He said, "However long it lasts, stay where you are. Do not leave the cabin. If the storm is as wild as I expect it to be, the bosun or the bosun's mate will strap you to your bunk. No protests, please, monsieur. I cannot allow a man as renowned and as needed as you are to take chances and perhaps suffer injuries. I speak to you now as your commander. You will do as I ask." Verrazzano bowed to him, turned quickly, and left the cabin.

Conflans did as he was bidden and remained in the cabin on the quarterdeck, the officers' deck between the poop and the mainmast.

Hurrying below, Verrazzano summoned the bosun.

"I was waiting for the summons, mon commandant. When do you think it will hit us?"

"That's difficult to say. Some storms break with scarcely any warning; others dally and build up for hours. Safety is not in guessing but in being prepared. If the pitching becomes severe, see to Captain Conflans. We cannot have any harm come to him. He objected, of course, but he is resigned now to being fastened to his bunk."

"Yes, monsieur."

"Right now," Verrazzano said, "I want all hands on deck."

The bosun, master of the crew, mustered the men.

Rapidly yet calmly, Verrazzano gave orders.

To some he said, "Furl the topsail. Bring down the staysails. Reef a portion of the mainsail."

To others, "Man the pumps."

To the bosun, "Rope two helmsmen to the poop. Permit sufficient length to move, but tie them fast. Then lash me to the sternpost near the helm. We are certain to need two men to hold the tiller. I can relieve one, then the other."

All was done, and not a minute too soon. With a speed that no one anticipated, the storm burst over the *Dauphine*. Thunder rumbled explosively. Lightning frescoed the duskiness with glittery blue zigzags that crackled and hissed like timber burning. The sky seemed to split wide open. Down came a deluge of rain. Gale winds turned the ocean into a fuming tumult and sent vast volumes of water crashing against the *Dauphine* and pouring over her decks. Wind and waves dragged her downward, held her, then let her go and pitched her high into space. She shuddered from stem to stern, righted herself, lurched downward, reared up, and plunged again. On and on. And all the while, Verrazzano rapped out orders, his voice competing with the storm's.

Together with his helmsmen he managed to keep his ship afloat. She shook, she strained, at times she was upended, at other times about to capsize. But, steered and worked by the strong hands and firm will of Verrazzano and his crew, she reelingly inched forward. For sixteen hours they fought for their ship and their lives. They whispered fragments of prayers, the short utterances of men in distress, the broken sentences of men struggling to survive. Sailors worked the wooden levers of the pumps without cease, and raised weals on their hands. For more than half a day the three on the poop shivered in blasts of glacial air as stabbing to the lungs as whiffs of ammonia to the nostrils. Too occupied to consider it, they suffered cold drenchings by rain and waves.

At last, at the end of the sixteenth hour the storm retreated on a low snarl of defeat. The *Dauphine*, like a white moth in all that blackness, her commander and his men, had won the long struggle and conquered their own realm, the sea.

Soaked and trembling with cold, Verrazzano shouted for the bosun to free them from the ropes that had saved them from going overboard.

As soon as he appeared, Verrazzano said, "Is everyone all right?"

"Yes, monsieur. Tired but unharmed."

"And Captain Conflans?"

"Fine, monsieur. I freed him half an hour ago. But," the bosun shook his head, "I doubt if Captain Conflans will let himself be kept down a second time."

Verrazzano smiled. He appreciated Conflans' annoyance, but he, Verrazzano, had named him captain of the *Dauphine* in deference to his seniority and fame. No harm must come to Antoine de Conflans, who knew more about ships than any man alive. In his specialized field he was peerless and indispensable. Verrazzano felt personally responsible for every man in his charge, and deeply responsible for Conflans.

Teeth chattering, he said, "Take apple brandy to Captain Conflans, and then give brandy to all. The men need warming up."

"Yes, monsieur. Thank you."

Verrazzano gripped the shoulders of his two helmsmen. "Brave, very brave, both of you," he said. "Get into dry clothing and take some rest."

Soon, weary but high-spirited sailors were in the rigging and on the yards to sheet home the canvas, and a new helmsman came to take the tiller.

Later, to all on board Verrazzano expressed his gratitude in typically simple words, "Well done, gentlemen. I am more grateful than I can say for your hard work and loyalty in this extreme difficulty. Thank you, *messieurs*. And God be praised."

Later still, Verrazzano sat at the table in his cabin, quill pen in his hand. A candle's flame threw a small pool of light upon his open *libretto,* a little book in which he kept a day-to-day account of the voyage. He wrote:

> This xxiiii day of February we suffered a tempest as severe as ever a man who has navigated suffered. From which, with the divine aid and the goodness of the ship ... we were delivered.

Once again a placid rhythm marked the voyage. Tranquil seas. Purring winds. Yet the farther the *Dauphine* advanced, the more Verrazzano worried about possible trouble. To himself he said, Pray that another storm does not swoop down and blow us to the south of west into Spain's New World waters. From now on he gave one unchanging order to the helmsmen, "Steer west, hold somewhat to the north."

They were not beset by another storm. They had remarkably easy sailing and again made excellent headway. As was his habit, Verrazzano estimated leagues and days from his last, not his first, point of embarkment. Not from Brittany, then, but from the "deserted rock," Europe had dissolved away from them by 1200 leagues (4800 miles) and almost fifty days.

*March 7.* Verrazzano wakened to a foggy, clammy dawn, hardly more than a slight dimming out of night. In a low wind the *Dauphine* snailed along through fog that rose from the sea's surface and rolled about like fallen clouds. The vapor was dense. So too was the hush.

Then suddenly from the crow's nest a sharp cry cut the silence.

"Lights! Lights!"

In a flash, Verrazzano was on the poop. He stared into the haze, but saw nothing.

"Lights where?" he called out to the sailor on the small enclosed platform near the masthead.

"Lights to port, monsieur."

At the port beam Verrazzano took a long look, but he still was unable to see anything.

"What kind of lights are they?" he shouted to the lookout.

"Fires, I think, monsieur."

"Do they seem to be far away or relatively close?"

"Perhaps a quarter of a league distant, monsieur."

"Do you see land, hills?"

"Not yet. But where there are lights there has to be land."

About that Verrazzano was not too sure. Dread stirred in him, not unlike the dread he had felt at the rock. There it was fear of capture by Portuguese, here it was fear of capture by Spaniards. There he had longed for the concealing darkness of night. Here he longed for revealing daylight. And the sun seemed reluctant to shine. The lights worried him. They could be cressets flaming on a fleet of Spanish galleons, or the fires of a Spanish land expedition. These were guesses only, but until wind and sun blew and burned away the heavy fog there was no knowing anything for certain.

Captain Conflans suddenly came up beside him. "I heard the lookout," he said. "Where are the lights?"

"Somewhere in that general direction." Verrazzano gestured with his hand. "From here they aren't visible yet."

"What lights are they?"

"The lookout thinks they are fires."

"Far away?"

"Maybe a quarter of a league," Verrazzano said, and wondered whether it was good or bad to be but one mile removed from the lights. He frowned and chewed his lip.

Conflans noticed the other's nervousness. It was the first time in all their months together that he had seen him disturbed. At the most crucial moments and in the most trying circumstances Verrazzano's judgment and calm were as decisive and cool as northern winds.

"Giovanni, are you troubled about those lights?"

"Yes, monsieur. A little."

"I see no need to be. We are in thirty-four degrees north latitude. This latitude doesn't include territory owned by Spain."

"Spaniards," said Verrazzano, "are apt to show up any day in any latitude. They are everywhere. Spain and Portugal find out what others are doing and where they are, but what do others find out about them? Only those things which they purposely wish to make known. We know, for example, that Spain's navigators find Magellan's road to the South Sea too long and too dangerous. It is no secret that Spaniards are on the hunt for a northwest passage to the Orient. We know that."

They also knew that Charles V issued grants to New World colonists who convinced him that they could find the passage. Royal cedulas—permits—already had been given to Hernando Cortés, the conqueror of Mexico, and to Lucas de Ayllón. A resident of Santo Domingo,

de Ayllón supposedly had discovered and claimed for
Spain the "land of Chicora," [5] later known as South
Carolina. Rumor had it that Cortés intended to explore
the coast from western Florida to Baccalaos.[6] Named
for the codfish that clogged the waters the way seaweed clogged the Sargasso Sea, Baccalaos, conforming
to the geographical concept of the day, contained Newfoundland, Nova Scotia, a part of Maine, and was linked
with Florida. Cortés expected to come upon the strait
somewhere between western Florida and Baccalaos.
Lucas de Ayllón believed the waterway shimmered in
northern Florida.

One non-colonist, Estevão Gomes, a Portuguese mariner in the service of Spain, also had received a license
from Charles V to search for the passage.[7]

On a forced note of optimism Verrazzano said, "The
royal cedulas are facts. The voyages which they permit
may or may not be facts." He glanced upward, saw the
sun vaguely. Blurry with haze, it looked like a tarnished
brass coin stuck upon the sky. "The sun is trying to come
through," he said, "and the wind is gaining a little.
Monsieur, what do you suggest?"

"Preparedness," Conflans replied. "Station armed sailors at the bulwarks. Man the two guns in the bow. For
officers, battle dress."

"*Tres bien,* monsieur. I will give the orders at once."

This done, Verrazzano went to his cabin. He donned
armor, removed his buckler from a peg on the wall of
his curtained bed-alcove, and for a long moment he
looked at it.

A work of art, the steel was polished to a high sheen

and was emblazoned with Verrazzano's shield-shaped crest. An eight-pointed wind rose, azure in color, flared from the center of the shield. The lily of Florence, a tri-petaled white iris, flowered at the top left. Wind rose and lily were divided by gold on the left and argent on the right. The motto on the crest was brief, consisting of only two words: *Più Chiaro,* Clearer.

Buckler on his arm, Verrazzano crossed the cabin and glanced out a porthole. The mist was fast evaporating. The sun threw a glow over the sea. Clearer. Much clearer. In this kind of clarity, the thought of being attacked by Spaniards was somehow unreasonable. The presence of Spaniards would spell surrender for himself and his men. "No!" he exclaimed to himself, "those lights cannot mean the end. They have to mean the beginning."

# 5

ᴡ WINDS blew and the sun burned away the whitish cocoon of mist. Clear now as the aqua sky was the view that opened upon an empty beryl-green ocean shaded with lapis, and a pale scallop of shores. No enemy fleet, no military encampment. Fires strung along the shores were dwindling to ashes. Here and there tatters of smoke fluttered upward. The folk who had kindled the fires were nowhere about. Obviously, they had seen the carrack with her great spread of canvas, taken fright, and fled inland. Or maybe they were in hiding behind the dunes.

Relieved at not having to confront a floating army of Spaniards, Verrazzano ordered every blade sheathed and fingers removed from the gun locks. Then, speechless with wonderment at having finally reached land, he scanned a coast which, it is believed, had not been visited by Europeans until Verrazzano and his men arrived in the *Dauphine*. Careful not to miss anything, he noted the lay of the land and the uneven shoreline of a chain of low-lying islands ridged with dunes. He described the dunes this way, "Fine sands, extending in

61

the shape of little hills xv feet high and perhaps fifty paces wide." [1] From this island-chain three headlands, one to the east, two to the southeast, jutted out into the Atlantic. Unnamed in 1524, later they were called Cape Hatteras, Cape Lookout, and Cape Fear. Verazzano's initial glimpse of America was of the southeast coast of North Carolina, at that time a nameless wilderness.[2] His landfall—in this case his first sighting of land from aboard ship—was a trifle to the south of Cape Fear, near what is now the port of Wilmington, at the head of the estuary of the Fear River.[3]

Waning beach fires and sand dunes are hardly spectacular. All the same, Verrazzano was absorbed in the distant scene.

Conflans watched him, saw the stern mouth smile, the black eyes sparkle. "Is it what you expected?"

"Even better, Captain. It is not like anything I ever read or heard about the New World. Quite different." Almost boyish in his anticipation of going ashore, he said, "We must land, find the people, and win their confidence." Impatience rang in his tone.

Amused, Conflans agreed that it offered an interesting prospect. "But," he said, "wouldn't it be helpful first of all to find a port?"

Verrazzano laughed. "I forgot! That shows you the measure of my excitement." He took a long look landward, to the north and to the south. "Around here, Captain, there is no port. What do you advise?"

Conflans advised searching for a port more to the south than to the north of their position.

So southward they sailed. After they had covered a considerable distance along a coast that began to seem as continuous as time, uneasiness mounted in Verrazzano.

"Captain, do you suppose we'll reach a harbor soon?"

"I've been asking myself the same question. No answer comes."

They could not know that a century or more would pass before harbors were founded on this coast. What they did know was their latitude, and it wasn't reassuring. They were near, possibly in, Lucas de Ayllón's Chicora.

"Usually I'm not a Job's comforter," Verrazzano said, "but aren't we inviting trouble by holding to a southerly course?" He paused, then thought aloud, "I shouldn't care to go there."

"You shouldn't care to go where, Giovanni?"

"Florida. Not at this particular time," he added, no longer as optimistic about Spanish expeditions not materializing as when he and Conflans discussed such dangers before the fog had lifted.

They both suddenly forgot about a southern harbor, forgot everything except the royal cedulas issued by Charles V in 1523 to Cortés, de Ayllón, and Gomes. Of the three, the one they most wanted to avoid was Estevão Gomes. A defector from Portugal to Spain, he sailed with Magellan, deserted, pirated away the ship *San Antonio,* and forced her captain and crew to return with him to Seville. A man not overtaxed with scruples, his was the dubious distinction of being held in low esteem by Peter Martyr, who opposed his ideas and wrote "I openly told him so." Nevertheless, Charles gave Gomes a permit to find for Spain a northwest passage to Cathay between Florida and Baccalaos.[4]

Far from Europe, Verrazzano and Conflans had no means of learning that their fears were groundless. Cortés was never to make the quest for a route to China. De Ayllón's expedition was put off for two years, and even then it was to end before it had half begun. In Spain, Gomes was attending the Council of Badajoz.[5] A bitter affair, experts from Spain and Portugal assembled to determine whether Portugal, who claimed the Moluccas (Spice Islands) and Sumatra, was entitled to that claim. Ultimately the decision favored Spain. Scientific calculations placed these Indian Ocean islands within the zone ceded to Spain in 1493 by Pope Alexander VI.

Unaware of what was happening in Mexico, Santo Domingo, and Badajoz, Verrazzano and his captain changed their course from south to north. In all they had logged fifty leagues when they came to a spot with good offshore anchorage, a little to the east of Cape Fear. Here they found themselves within easy reach of a shore that was brown with beelike clusters of Indians.[6]

The mixed crew of Normans and Italians stood at the rails and stared curiously at the natives, who returned their stares with equal curiosity. Never before had these Europeans seen Indians. It seems almost equally certain that the Indians had never until then seen Europeans. Their manifest amazement gives weight to the belief that white men were unknown to the natives.

Jet-shiny heads, many adorned, Verrazzano noted, "with garlands of birds' feathers," were lifted toward him. It was as if they recognized the leader, for his air of command was as patent as the erectness of his bearing.

"We are being rudely silent," he said to his men. "Let us show some mark of friendliness." Verrazzano set the example. He waved and called out greetings in his own tongue. Italian seamen joined him. The Normans shouted lustily in French.

Startled, not sure if this babel was amiable or hostile, the Indians began to retreat. Yet even in their uncertainty they admired the strangers. Repeatedly they halted and looked up at the men on the ship before they proceeded another few steps.

"Don't go away! We will not harm you. Come back. Please do not be afraid. Come back!" Appeal and assurance mingled in Verrazzano's voice and somehow carried the meaning of his words. Quickly, gladly the Indians returned to the beach and sent up a prolonged ear-splitting yell.

"*Quelle tapage!*" exclaimed Conflans.

"Nothing to worry about, Captain. That uproar is cordial."

"Cordial?"

"Yes. It is their way of giving welcome, I think. Yes it is. See? They are calling and beckoning to us." Verrazzano turned to Conflans. "Monsieur, the people are friendly and eager to prove it. You and twelve sailors are going ashore with presents for them."

"No," said Conflans, and shook a finger at Verrazzano. "I am staying right here. Your courtesy is without fault, Giovanni. In deference to my seniority you offer me the honor. But this is your landfall, nobody else's. Fetch some presents. I'll order the boat lowered and have the bosun line up twelve men."

"Thank you, monsieur. Beyond that," said Verrazzano simply, "I cannot say what I feel."

The captain gave a short laugh. "I'd be the last to doubt that. You bury your heart so deeply that your feelings rarely show and even more rarely shape up into words. Go, now," he said, and gave Verrazzano's shoulder a paternal thump.

Not long after, Giovanni da Verrazzano, accompanied by twelve sailors, set foot for the first time on American soil. Indians beached the boat. The chieftain greeted them in his own strange-sounding dialect. Then, preceded by the chieftain and two braves, Verrazzano walked with regal dignity toward the waiting crowd of natives. His sailors followed, wide-eyed and fascinated.

While the women hastened to prepare food, Verrazzano did exactly what he would have done if he were being feted in Florence or in Greve. He made a speech. Aided by expressive use of hands and arms, he conveyed his feeling for the beauty of the shores and thanked the Indians for the gracious way they had received him and his men. A master stroke, this short address, for Indians of nearly every tribe were as enamored of oratory as any Italian. They did not understand a word of what he said, but words seemed not to matter. His ready eloquence, the directness of his glance and his Tuscan composure persuaded them that he was to be trusted. They felt no need to be on guard against some sudden act of treachery.

His thanks spoken, Verrazzano motioned to a mariner

who stepped forward and held a carved wooden box filled with a dazzling assortment of baubles. As ceremoniously as if he were bestowing the blazoned brocade banners (*palii*) to the winner of the *Corso,* Florence's famed horse race, he presented to the chieftain a splendid rope of red and blue glass beads the size of hazel nuts. Catching the light, the glass shone like spurts of ruby and drops of solidified blue sea-water. Proudly, the chief hung the beads round his neck. Now Verrazzano distributed among the others a twinkling heap of necklaces, bracelets, scarlet caps, mirrors, toys, and that perennial favorite of Indians since the coming of Christopher Columbus in 1492, thimble size hawk bells of polished brass. Enchanted, they chattered back and forth and showed delight in the stately, flashing-eyed man with hair as black as theirs, but short and wavy, not "shoulder length and straight, and tied back in the form of a little tail," as Verrazzano later described the hair style of the Indian men and boys. Women and girls wore twin braids, one dangling over each shoulder.

Encouraged by the gently humorous look on his face and the softness of his voice, children forgot their shyness and approached him. Their bright black eyes peeped up at his own, their lips echoed his smile. His gold neckchain, he discovered, did not attract them or the grownups. They apparently had no gold and no liking for the metal that Europeans valued over any other. A similar indifference to gold, he recalled, had been peculiar to the natives Columbus came upon in the West Indies. What bedazzled the little Indians was his attire. The manner of his dress, and silk itself, was foreign to them. Gazes were riveted on his lavender velvet garb with cape lining, sleeves, and trunk slashes of emerald taffeta. Small brown hands patted the fabrics lightly, as though aware that the silks were costly. Every time he moved the children laughed and danced about him, intrigued by the crispy swish of taffeta.

Men, women, and children, Verrazzano observed, were clad more or less alike. All had animal skins draped diagonally across the chest. Kiltlike girdles fashioned of coon tails and cloth of woven grasses hung from waist to knee. Men and boys, and a few women, wore headbands of feathers.

A nobleman accustomed to the society of intellectuals, Verrazzano, to the amazement of his mariners, adapted himself without difficulty to his primitive hosts, made himself understood, and with a warmth they hadn't guessed he possessed, he showed himself to be as genuinely at ease with illiterate aborigines as with his peers. The riddle, if it was that, had a simple answer. Verrazzano regarded all peoples as human beings, and in their humanness no different from himself.

Having nothing else to give in return for the cherished trinkets, the Indians offered food, and with courtly grace Verrazzano accepted for his men and himself. The meal was tasty. The guests dined heartily on rounds of bread baked of Indian maize, fish broiled over coals, and wild berries threaded with honey. Verrazzano and his men may well have been the first Europeans to sample southern hospitality on these shores.

Sunset turned the ocean into liquid fire opal. It was time to go. Indians loaded the boat with maize, gourdfuls of fresh water, and armfuls of wood. Youngsters scampered to the tops of dunes to get a better view of the leave-taking. Together with their elders they shouted farewells. His short cape flung back over one shoulder, Verrazzano stood in the boat and waved, answering their good-bys with *addios* and *adieus*.

The screech of oarlocks ceased. Verrazzano deftly scaled the ship's ladder. On deck once more, he looked reflectively at the site of his actual landfall in America. And of this land, later to be known as North Carolina, one feels that Giovanni da Verrazzano can with reason be called the discoverer.

"How was it?" Conflans inquired.

"Splendid, monsieur. Wonderful."

"The people appear to have been congenial and generous."

"Oh, very."

"At close range are they more or less alike in appear-rance?"

"More or less, yes." After a moment, Verrazzano gave Conflans essentially the same details that he was to put in writing four months from now. He said:

> They are of a dark brown color, rather like Ethi-opians.[7] Their hair is black, thick, and straight . . . They are well proportioned and of medium stature, although some exceed us in height. They tend somewhat to broadness in the face. Not a few, how-ever, are fine-featured. Their eyes are black and large, the glance intent and quick. They do not seem to have unusual physical strength, but they are extremely agile and it is easy to believe they are tireless runners.

Captain Conflans asked, "Do they bear a likeness to any peoples you have seen in other countries?"

"Yes, they look like Orientals, particularly those of the remotest Sinarian regions." [8] Verrazzano inhaled deeply of the clean salt-tanged air, then he said, "Our first visit ashore bodes well for what lies ahead."

Slowly the *Dauphine* began to roll through the chalk-blue dusk to a cove the Indians had pointed out to Verrazzano as a safe spot to anchor for the night.

The next morning at daybreak they upped anchor.

Dunes soon gave way to woodland. Verrazzano wrote:

> Nearby appears spacious land with lovely plains covered with large forests . . . clothed in foliage of as many hues as there are trees, and more beautiful than it would be possible to express . . . These are nothing like the forests of Hyrcania [9] or the wild solitudes of Scythia and northern countries, full of rugged trees, but are adorned with palms, laurels, cypresses, and trees unknown in our Europe . . . For great distances they exude the sweetest odor . . . The forests are alive with stags, deer, and hares. There are many lakes and pools, and a vast variety and number of birds. This land we named *Selva di Lauri* [Laurel Woods]. Farther along, we gave the name *Campo di Cedri* [Field of Cedars] to a field of handsome cedars. We caught their fragrance whenever the people happened to be burning the trees and the wind blew from the land.

By day the *Dauphine* followed the coastline. Verrazzano took care not to lose sight of the sandy foreshores.

He also took frequent soundings, and made certain that before they dropped anchor for the night the carrack had deep water beneath her keel. He was vigilant, charmed, and observant, as can be gathered from these words:

> The air is healthy and pure, and neither hot nor cold. Gentle winds blow. The prevailing winds are west-north-west. The sky is serene and clear, as in Damascus. Rains are infrequent ... The sea is tranquil ... And even though the shore inclines to lowness and has no harbors, it is not bothersome for sailors, for it is free of rocks and shoals and is so deep that within four or five paces from land are found, exclusive of flood or ebb tides, xx feet of water increasing in a uniform proportion to the depth of the sea with such perfect holding-ground that any ship at all, even if assailed by a storm, can never perish here, unless it breaks its rope and loses its anchor. ...

By night the *Dauphine* was able to anchor inshore, due to the nature of the coast. Nightlong fires flared up and down these shores, the sands crimsoned by the flames. As on a mountain lake, faraway sounds carried with intense clarity. Owls cried. Frogs chirruped at the edges of marsh ponds. Sometimes a bird's sharp whistle blew past the moon that seemed ensnared in the cordage of the *Dauphine's* tall mainmast. Sometimes Indians emerged hush-footedly from the forest, threw another few sticks of wood on their fires, and disappeared like phantoms. Disquieting to the men on the *Dauphine* was the nocturnal dissonance of drums, gourd rattles shaken with staccato vigor, and the upward whine of Indian flutes. The faintly sinister element in the atmosphere was accented by the whispery rustle of fan-shaped palmetto leaves clashing in the wind. "Palms" Verrazzano termed them, not incorrectly, for the palmetto is cousin to the dwarf palm he was familiar with in southern Europe and North Africa.

The odors that perfumed the air were heaviest at night, and evoked emotions and memories. Night and its indefinable scents made the mariners long for home.

"We must have been mad to volunteer for this voyage. Why did we?"

"Because we admire and have faith in Verrazzano."

"Had faith."

"No, our faith in him and in his goal is unimpaired," said the blond young Norman who was simply Matelot —Sailor—to Verrazzano. The youth took it for what it was, a mark of favor.

"You are right. Still, at times one wonders."

"I know. After nightfall one wonders about many things. At night we anchor in a world that doesn't seem in the least like the world we see in daytime."

"Matelot," the other sailor said, "what do you suppose monsieur le commandant thinks about when he walks the deck late into the night?"

"Home and relatives, I guess. He's no different from the rest of us, except he is lonelier."

"Did he say that?"

"Of course not. He wouldn't, ever. He doesn't have to say it. You can see it in his eyes. Maybe he is a lonely man by nature. Maybe it's because he is the commander. Once I heard him tell Brunelleschi that he had discovered the loneliness of leadership, the aloneness of command. Besides, he is a voluntary exile who never really left his homeland."

This was true. No matter where Verrazzano might be—Egypt, Syria, Turkey, North Africa, Greece, France, America—he was in Italy also. He existed in two places at the same time, the land he was in and the one which held his heart—Italy. What with his rule of no night-sailing on uncharted coasts, Verrazzano found the hours long; he grew as restless as the fires that waved, rose, sank, and rose again. He paced the poop. He halted, stood at the rail and stared into the featureless dark. He pictured a dock and people, and beyond the dock roof-tops and church cupolas. Then he would seem to wait, as if for bells to chime the hour. His thoughts were in Florence and Greve where bells rang out night and day. Frogs and wild turkeys were the only time-tellers here, other than the sun. The raspy croak of frogs announced the onset of day's end. Wild turkeys, roosting in the heights of magnolias whose huge flowers resembled water lilies blooming on trees, heralded sunup with a raucous clamor. Verrazzano, like his sailors, succumbed to the low mood induced at night by eerie sounds and perfume that floated like the smoke of some ever-burning incense. Acacia? Jasmine? Angelica? Helio-trope? To no avail, he tried to analyze the properties in the haunting blend of scents. America's wilderness fas-cinated him, but its nights and fragrances made him homesick.

Verrazzano did not dispute the feeling. Instead, he

retired to his cabin, wrote copiously in his libretto, and
started letters. These remained unfinished. Finally he
tore them up and tossed the flakes of paper into the
ocean. He eased his sense of remissness by reminding
himself that upon his return to France he would write a
full report to the king and send similar letters to family
members and friends. And so in this manner another
night would pass. As soon as a new dawn rose-tinted the
sea, the world became real again. Daylight and the
open sea combined to banish nostalgia and discouragement. The *Dauphine* moved on, always skirting the
coast which now, after eighteen days, took a turn to
the east.

*March 25.*[10] A day of blue-crystal brightness. Verrazzano's vivid imagination imprinted upon the air domed
and towered Florence. Today his banner-draped city
was marking two festivities in one: the Feast of the
Annunciation and the Florentine New Year.[11] He was
there in his imagination. A flock of bells pealed from
Giotto's marble-banded stalk of a *campanile*. Prelates in
jewel-quivering vestments celebrated Mass in the great
*Duomo*, Cathedral of *Santa Maria del Fiore*—St. Mary
of the Flower. Later, an image of the Virgin was carried through piazzas and streets on a golden litter
heaped with lilies. Mounted nobles, eight in number,
escorted the litter. Riding slowly on plumed steeds ca-
parisoned in cloth of gold, the *cavalieri* sat erect in
their saddles, their gilded lances at rest. On this gala
*giorno dell' Annunziata,* Florence glowed with silks and
burnished lances, silks and silver trumpets, in honor of
St. Mary of the Flower.

Verrazzano led his men in prayer but felt that this was not enough.

"A few prayers," he said unhappily to Captain Conflans, "a meager tribute for a Florentine to Our Lady!"

"*Eh bien*, Giovanni, at sea what more can you do?"

He soon knew what more he could do. He was sailing a blue radiance of water. Nearby shores were green swells of leafage crested with the pink foam of laurel and redbud. Above the waves of greenery flowers of the sassafras tree flaunted their sunny yellow. Sassafras exhaled the heliotrope odor.

"How beautiful!" exclaimed Verrazzano.

"It is, it is," Conflans agreed.

Happiness in his voice now, Verrazzano said, "I know a way to honor the day, my city, and the shores."

"Do you? How?"

"We will baptize this lovely unchristened coast *Annunziata*."

The name was given, and Verrazzano made a note of the event in Latin, in his libretto. But, even as the blossoms that inspired him were destined to bloom but for a brief time, so too the Italian name he gave these shores was destined, like a short-lived flower, to pale away into obscurity. One part of Annunziata later came to be called Carolina, the other part Virginia.

Farther east, Verrazzano saw glinty wind-crinkled silver. Not sure whether it was water or a mirage, he waited a bit, then he shouted to the sailor in the crow's nest, "*Eh, la!* Do you see water to the west?"

"Yes, monsieur."

In French, Verrazzano asked, "Does it seem to be a large lake?"

"*Non,* monsieur. *Une mer!*" A sea.

Verrazzano's heart leapt high, as the heart of Columbus had leapt when he sighted land October 12, 1492, and thought he was in Asia. Verrazzano knew this was not Asia, but he believed he had found the prize, a northwest passage to Asia. Merely to see the water from afar was to picture a cargo of gems, gold, silks, teakwood, and spices. Presently he became aware of an isthmus. It barred his way to what he called "the oriental sea." Now he ran northward, confident of being able to circumvent the barrier and enter the passage by means of a strait or a northerly cape. Bitterly disappointed, he later wrote:

> We found an isthmus one mile wide and about 200 long, in which, from the ship, was seen the oriental sea between the west and the north, which is the one, without doubt, which circles round the extremity of India and Cathay . . . We navigated along the said isthmus with the constant hope of finding some strait or promontory at which the land would end toward the north and thus permit us to penetrate to the blessed shores of Cathay. . . .

There was no entry.

Scholars hold differing opinions as to the locality of Verrazzano's "oriental sea," by which he meant an arm of the Pacific, not the enormous ocean itself. Some think that what he saw was either Pamlico or Albemarle Sound, as they are called today. To others, it was the

Delaware or Chesapeake Bay. Still others maintain that Verrazzano failed to see either the Delaware or the Chesapeake, a fairly common failure among navigators who sailed these coasts after 1524. Conversely, there are geographers who are convinced that Verrazzano saw Chesapeake Bay and mistook it for a tributary of the Pacific. His visual estimate of the so called "sea" being "one mile wide and about 200 long," leads one to think that Chesapeake Bay may have been the body of water that he sighted. At its narrowest point it is four miles in width, and it extends for 200 miles, as compared to the North Carolina Sounds, each fifty or sixty miles in length, and Delaware Bay's seventy miles.

The only indisputable fact in this whole mix-up is that Verrazzano wrongly believed, for a time at least, that the inlet—whichever one it was—offered egress to the South Sea. He made a mistake. What is amazing is not that he and other explorers of unexplored regions made mistakes, but that they made so few. They sailed without the benefit of the navigational tables and instruments developed in later centuries. Navigating in 1524 differed little from navigating in 1492. No important changes occurred in navigation during the three decades that followed the first landfall of Christopher Columbus in the New World. Far from perfect, the means of making nautical observations accounted for many errors. Even experienced navigators like Verrazzano and Conflans were capable of miscalculating to the extent of one degree or more, and according to Verrazzano's nautical notes he "allowed for each degree 62½ miles."

Due to the unreachable "oriental sea," Verrazzano formed his own idea of the shape of America, an erroneous yet logical concept in view of his geographical beliefs at this time. He saw it as a double continent linked by a strip of land, the Atlantic rolling up its waves on one side of the isthmus, the South Sea, or a part of it, on the other. European cartographers were to depict Verrazzano's notion on their maps for years and years. Before the end of his exploration Verrazzano would radically alter his original opinion in regard to the geographical kinship between America and Asia. And while navigators followed in his wake to find his "oriental sea," not many, it seems, meditated on his significant conclusion. He put it this way:

> This land or New World . . . is one, connected together. It does not adjoin Asia or Africa (which I know to be a certainty). It may join Europe by Norway and Russia, which would be false according to the ancients. They declare almost all the north from the promontory of the Cimbri [12] to have been navigated to the east, going around as far as the Caspian Sea . . . Thus, it would remain included between two seas, the Eastern and the Western, and that, consequently, closes off the one from the other. For beyond 54 degrees from the equator toward the south it [the new land] stretches toward the east for a great distance, and from the north passing 66 degrees it continues, turning toward the east, reacting as far as 70 degrees. . . .[13]

Verrazzano's correct deduction that America stood alone, unrelated to Asia and Africa, canceled out the "oriental sea." He arrived at the full appreciation of this truth after a month or so had passed. Yet, for some unfathomable reason, he failed to delete the "oriental sea" from his map and his notes. Even more puzzling is the fact that he mentioned the non-existent sea in his Letter to the King and in semi-copies of the letter.

The map of Vesconte de Maggiolo, made in 1527 and based largely on information provided by Verrazzano, shows the *Mare Indicum* in the area of what is now Virginia. Verrazzano's map-maker brother, Girolamo, placed it in almost the same position on his map of 1529.[14] Other maps, Michael Lok's for one, dated 1582, portrayed Verrazzano's double-continent picture and set what was commonly called the Sea of Verrazzano in the locale of Chesapeake Bay. For the next one hundred years this will-o'-the-wisp of a "sea" was to addle otherwise clear-headed navigators.

*March 27.* A sense of guilt needled Verrazzano. An Italian exile sailing under the egis of the king of France, he hadn't yet named so much as a grove for his Majesty. So today, in the presence of the ship's company, he formally baptized "all the land found" in honor of Francis I. To the French it was *La Francescane;* to the Italians, *La Francesca.* The name covered not only all the land found since March 7, but was intended to include whatever more Verrazzano was still to find.

Fifty leagues later he came upon "another land." Charmed by it, Verrazzano anchored here for three days. Due to his strictly enforced rule that the *Dauphine* must never be left without a pilot on board, he and Captain Conflans took turns going ashore. But

Verrazzano possessed a curiosity and enthusiasm about the unknown wilds that Conflans lacked. More navigator than explorer, Antoine de Conflans usually chose to stay with the ship and let Verrazzano explore the shores.

A naturalist and poet at heart, Verrazzano reveled in this place. On each of the three days he tramped four miles or more, through forests of trees taller than Tuscan cypresses and swagged with long loops of morning-glory and trumpet-flower vines, the blue blossoms of the one, the pumpkin-colored blossoms of the other, hanging in great clusters. Sunshine sifting through their canopies of heavy leafage was more like thin green mist than sunlight. Other trees, not as tall, were twisted and hunched, their branches bearded with a mosslike plant that hung in long gray strands. He lingered in thickets of wild roses, was astonished to see here and there a pale purple blur of violets. He walked in sunless spaces where the duskiness was lit only by small white hepatica flowers. He found rapture in a singing tree, in flashes of bright wings—red birds, tanagers the scarlet of nasturtiums, black-and-gold orioles, and fluting brown thrashers. Few details escaped him. He gives the following condensed picture:

> We found the people here to be of lighter color than the others.[15] They clothe themselves in certain grasses which grow pendent from the trees. This they weave with various ends of hemp. The head is bare ... Their food is pulse of excellent flavor; also game, fish, and birds which they catch with bows and snares. The bow is fashioned of sturdy

wood, the arrow of reed, tipped with bone of fishes or animals. . . .

Their barges are constructed from a single tree twenty feet long and four feet wide. They are not made with instruments of stone, iron, or other metals . . . Instead, they use fire, burning a sixth part of the wood as suffices for the hollow of the boat, also of the stern and prow, so that in navigating, it is possible to plow the waves of the sea. . . .

Vines of natural growth abound here. Rising, they entwine themselves around the trees, as they do in Cisalpine Gaul [Northern Italy]. If these people had our system of [grape] culture, there is no doubt they would produce good wines. Often we tasted the dry fruit of those vines and found it sweet and agreeable, not different from ours. . . .

We found wild roses, violets, and lilies, and many sorts of herbs and fragrant flowers unfamiliar to us. We did not see their houses, having gone only two leagues inland. However, by what we were able to learn from the people, their dwellings are of wood and tough grasses, and we believe that many of the people, sleeping on the ground, have no roof except the sky. . . .

In this land we found a man who came to the shore to see what people we were. He stood hesitating and ready for flight . . . He was handsome, nude, of olive color, his hair fastened back in a knot. We were about twenty in number and, coaxing him, he approached, holding a burning stick as if to offer us a gift of fire. And we showed him how we make fire with powder and flint-and-steel, and he trembled with terror. Then he stopped as if astonished, and prayed, worshipping like a monk, lifting his finger toward the sky, and, pointing to the ship and the sea, he appeared to bless us.

The wilderness of flower-festooned trees evidently put Verrazzano in mind of Vergil, Italy's early poet of Mantua. Enamored of Arcadia, legendary home of Pan, the Grecian god of rural folk, Vergil lyricized Arcadia as the epitome of pastoral beauty. Verrazzano left an echo of Vergil in America when he christened this paradise of trees *Arcadia*. Echoes die. This Vergilian echo died when the region was renamed Maryland.

The three-day stay at an end, Verrazzano navigated toward the north and east, and told himself that from now on he must give precedence to place names pleasing to the royal family and to the king's favorite courtiers. As a reminder, he jotted down the names of personages to whom diplomacy required him to pay regard. Not in order of rank, but simply as they came to him, he listed the names: Jean de Guise, Cardinal of Lorraine; Duke of Alençon and Anjou; Admiral Bonnivet; Count de St. Pol; Duke of Vendôme; Marguerite of Angoulême, sister of the king; Louise of Savoy, mother of the king. These were all the names of living persons. When Verrazzano embarked from Dieppe, it was rumored that Queen Claude was gravely ill and not expected to live. Not knowing whether she was alive or dead, he omitted her name.

On. On. North-northeast.

The days were clear and cool, the nights pricked with the brilliance of stars. Peaceful landscapes replaced the scenery of the semi-tropical South with its exotic touches and tarrying perfume. Verrazzano remained alert for an entry into the "oriental sea," but none appeared. Instead, he found a verdant hedgerow of a coast backed by forests. Apple-green here, goldish-green there, with pastel tintings of lady's-slipper pink, creamy white, and bright yellow. A coast worthy of a cardinal, Verrazzano dubbed it *La Costa di Lorenna,* the Coast of Lorraine. Its first known name, *Lorenna,* vanished when it became New Jersey.

In mid-April [16] Verrazzano sighted two promontories. They did not lead to the South Sea but they decreased the names on his list by two. He called the one *Promontorio Lanzone* (Alençon), the other *Promontorio Bonivetto* (Bonnivet). A man of letters, whenever Verrazzano alluded to a cape or headland he used the literary form *promontorio* rather than *capo.* Shortly, he turned amazed eyes on a little hill—*monticello*—that stood by the sea. Having sailed 100 leagues of flat coast, a bluff a few hundred feet high looked to him like a hill. A rarity, he gave it the name *San Polo,* for the Count de St. Pol. What came next into his line of vision amazed him still more. Contained within "two little eminences" were green shores and cinnamon-skinned Indians. Between the two hills there "flowed to the sea a very great river." He gives this account:

Due to being anchored off the coast in good shelter, we did not wish to venture in without knowledge of the entrances. We therefore took the small boat and entered the river to the land, which we found heavily populated.

The people, similar to the others, clothed with the feathers of birds of various colors, came toward us joyfully, uttering loud exclamations of welcome, and showed us where we could land most safely with the boat.

We entered the river, within the land, about half a league, where we saw that it made a very beautiful lake within a circuit of about three leagues. Thence which the people went, going from one and another part to the number of xxx of their little barges, with innumerable people, who passed from one shore and the other in order to see us. . . .

Immensely impressed by the majestic river, Verrazzano felt that it deserved a princely name. He baptized it *Vandoma* after the Duke of Vendôme, prince of the blood.

Verrazzano's "very beautiful lake" was not a lake. It was a bay, an arm of the Atlantic Ocean. Today the bay is divided into the Upper Bay and the Lower Bay. The entire bay is enclosed by the shores of northeast New Jersey, Staten Island, Manhattan Island, and Brooklyn. To the southeast, the bay opens into the ocean. The Narrows, a strait two miles long and one mile in width, connects the upper and lower bays, and separates Brooklyn and Staten Island.

With Norman sailors at the oars, Verrazzano was rowed through the Narrows eighty-five years before the bay and the river Vandoma were seen by Henry Hudson. An English navigator, Hudson was sent by the Dutch East India Company to find a northwest passage to Asia. In 1609, navigating the *Half Moon* of Amsterdam, he followed Verrazzano's trail. Hudson cannot really be said to have discovered the river to which the Dutch gave his name, but he undoubtedly was the first European to explore its 300 miles of water.

Stunned by what they were seeing, Verrazzano and his companions viewed this land in silence, while a multitude of Indians on shore and on the water in canoes—Verrazzano uses the word *barca,* barge—let go with the traditional Indian yell of greeting. The moment the Europeans landed, natives came from all directions to meet and admire the strangers. The Indians were reddish-brown in color, their black and shiny hair caught up in tufts; their eyes were black and somewhat slanted. The feather apparel they wore was a far cry from the feather mantles Jean Fleury had captured from the Spanish treasure galleon. These "feathers of birds of various colors" were not brilliantly green, flamingo, and peacock-blue powdered with chips of turquoises and jade. The Indians had no jewels, no collars dripping golden bells and opals, no ritual masks of gem-mosaics. They were not Aztecs; not Manhattans either. One of the nine tribes of the Wappinger Confederacy, the Manhattans did not appear on the banks of the Hudson until the seventeenth century. The name of these Indians, who doubtless had their roots in the Algonquian stock, mattered no more to Verrazzano than had the names of other Indians. More important to him than tribal names was the Indians' attitude. So far, all the natives he had encountered were friendly. This he appreciated, and the Indians appreciated his demeanor toward them. Dignified and kindly in his dealings with the Indians, Verrazzano unfailingly inspired a happy response. A true Christian humanist, all men to him were his fellow-men, regardless of color and race, regardless of whether their culture was Florentine Renaissance or American Woodland.

The island and the "beautiful lake" held him spellbound. In turn, the simple Indians were spellbound by his presents of colored beads, hawk bells, and coral *paternostri*, rosaries. His visit, however, was necessarily brief. He gives the reason:

> In an instant, as is apt to happen to navigators, a gale of unfavorable wind blowing from the sea, we were forced to return to the ship, leaving the land with great regret because of its spaciousness and beauty. . . .

Prior to casting off, Verrazzano christened the wide blue bay *Santa Margherita,* the saint's name of the king's sister. To the land itself he gave the name *Angoulême,* in honor of Francis I who, before he became king, was the Duke of Angoulême. A bell-chiming name, Angoulême, it was the first non-Indian identity ever given to what is now the city of New York.

Late in the year 1524, Estevão Gomes set sail from Spain and repeated Verrazzano's voyage. In January, 1525, he reached Verazzano's Angoulême. He changed the name of the bay from Santa Margherita to *San*

*Antonio*. For a saint or for the ship *San Antonio* that he stole from the fleet of Ferdinand Magellan? The answer can only be guessed at. All the land that he saw he named for himself—*La Tierra de Gomes*, The Land of Gomes. He returned by the same route he had come. Having found neither gold, spices, nor a passage to the Orient, he lured to his ship kindly Indians on the shores of Verrazzano's Arcadia and Annunziata and took them captive. Some he sold in Santo Domingo, the others he took to Spain to be sold into slavery there.[17] As far as is known, these people, kidnapped by Gomes, were the first Indians of what is now the United States ever to be enslaved. With their capture, Indian cordiality on the coasts that Verrazzano had sailed came to a prolonged end. In this region, Indian esteem and trust of the white man soured into hatred and suspicion.

In 1626 the Dutchman, Peter Minuit, bought Angoulême from the natives for a supposed twenty-four dollars' worth of trifles. Dutch settlers baptized the area New Netherland and built New Amsterdam, their capital, at the southern tip of the island. Thirty-eight years later the British arrived and seized it from the Dutch. Under British rule, this coveted location which, in the space of a century, was called Angoulême, *La Tierra de Gomes*, and New Netherland, received still another name—New York.

Whether Giovanni da Verrazzano was or was not the discoverer of what is now the City of New York is a matter that perhaps is open to debate. It seems more than likely, however, that the distinction belongs to him. If any other explorer was in the same locality before mid-April, 1524, no document has come to light to prove it. The most valuable of Verrazzano's several accounts of his voyage found its way to his close friend, Cardinal Paolo Giovio of Como. By inheritance, the same letter came into the possession of a Roman nobleman, Count Giulio Macchi di Cellere.[18] Discovered in his library 385 years after it was written, the Count permitted its English translation and publication in the United States. Unless another authentic codex concerning the New York area turns up, pre-dating Verrazzano's letter of July 8, 1524, one may safely agree with Count di Cellere's positive statement in a message to Edgar H. Hall, the American translator of the Cellere Codex. The Count's letter is headed, "Villa Cellere, Tor Pignatarra, Rome, January 27, 1910." It reads, in part:

> I am very pleased to hear you take such a deep interest in the document which can well be considered the birth certificate of New York, and that the manuscript will be made known to the American government, as it proves *to a certainty when, how, and who* first discovered the land that was to be the cradle of the great city of New York....

It was with reluctance that Verrazzano left Angoulême, and his final observation hinted of prophecy. He pictured it as a commodious port capable of sustaining fleets of cargo ships. He wrote:

> From the sea to the estuary of the river, which is very deep within the mouth, laden ships might pass without difficulty, aided by the tide which we found to rise eight feet....

His vision has materialized. The port of New York is the largest commercial port in the United States. The harbor supports immense traffic and has docking facilities on three shores—Manhattan, Brooklyn, and New Jersey.

The explorer had no thought of being remembered. On the contrary, he accepted it as natural to go unremembered, for he had known more than one great man who was robbed of glory within his lifetime and forgotten after he was dead. But 400 years later New York City's Verrazano-Narrows Bridge,[19] the world's longest suspension bridge—its 4,260 feet spanning the Narrows between Brooklyn and Staten Island—commemorates Giovanni da Verrazzano's life of service, his brave voyage of 1524, and his discovery of New York.

Blown out of Angoulême by a squall, the *Dauphine* soon swept past the shores of today's Long Island. Springtime lay over the coast like a veil of misted green with a profusion of flowers and unfolding buds painted on it. Verrazzano's poetic sensibilities received and retained pictorial impressions. In this instance they probably accounted for the name that identifies Long Island on the renowned 1527 map of his Genoese friend, Vesconte de Maggiolo. The name is *Flora*—in Roman mythology the goddess of gardens and flowers.

Continuing eastward, "as thus the land turned," Verrazzano made another, if smaller, discovery:

Having traveled lxxx leagues, always in sight of land, we found an island triangular in form, distant x leagues from the continent, in size like the

> Island of Rhodes, full of wooded hills and well populated, judging by the many fires burning all along the surrounding shore. . . .

This island that reminded Verrazzano either of Rhodes, the capital of a group of islands southwest of Turkey, or of a small seaport of the same name on the island-capital, he baptized *La Isola Aloysia* (Luisa) in honor of Louise of Savoy, mother of King Francis I. Although he wanted to anchor and explore this island, strong gusts and an April downpour prevented him.

Ninety years later the Dutch explorer, Adrian Block, sighted this little island which is off the coast of modern Rhode Island. It was given his name and is still known as Block Island.

*April 22.* In a spate of pale sunshine that took some of the chill out of the air, Verrazzano and his men came to yet another land where, in Verrazzano's words, "we found a port of very great beauty. . . ."

This port, in southwest Rhode Island, was at the entrance of Narragansett Bay, an arm of the Atlantic. It was not long before a line of twenty canoes filled with Indians appeared, but "fifty paces" away from the *Dauphine* the oarsmen, with a backward sweep of their paddles, brought their canoes to a stop. Intrigued and baffled, the Indians gazed up at the white carrack with a rainbow dolphin on her prow, and bannered with two flags. One was centered with a scarlet cross, the other with three golden fleurs-de-lis, the royal emblem of France.[20] Gazes strayed from the dolphin and the high-flying ensigns to the waving sailors at the deck rails.

Then, as always happened, Indian attention shifted to the stately presence of Verrazzano and lingered on him. Standing on the open pavilion of the poop, he cut a regal figure in garnet velvet, deep red against the pallid blue sky. He was, they decided, the chieftain. Captain Conflans joined him. The older man also looked distinguished. He, too, must be a chieftain.

"Come closer, come," Verrazzano called out and beckoned them.

Although they understood his sign language they were timid.

He motioned to them to draw nearer. "Come," he urged, "come."

Not certain whether they should or should not do as he asked, the boatmen stood in their canoes, turned toward their two sachems and made inquiries in their Algonquian dialect. Each of the two chieftains (Verrazzano refers to them as "kings") sat in his own long canoe with his attendants. They agreed that they liked the stranger's looks, his manner, his voice, and his dark red attire. He was a man to be trusted. The reply they gave their people was Yes.

Immediately, the Indians sent up a happy shout of welcome and the armada began to move, slowly, quietly. There was no rattle of oarlocks. The wide-bladed paddles were used without oarlocks, one of several features of Indian canoes that never ceased to amaze the *Dauphine's* men. In graceful formation the canoes encircled the ship. Then the men let their paddles rest.

Near enough now for Verrazzano to throw to them

the best of what was left of his dwindled supply of "*fantasie*," his word for baubles, he peered into the chest a sailor held open, and said, distressed, "What will we do? We haven't enough to go around." His distress was needless, as he was soon to find out. Fingering through what remained, he selected the better necklaces and bracelets and earrings, little mirrors in gilt frames, and the shiniest hawk bells. From stern to prow, from port to starboard he went, in order to distribute the gifts on all sides as best he could. Deftly he tossed them through the air. Deft hands were cupped to catch them. Dark eyes examined the articles. The people looked up at him, smiled, and shook their heads.

More to their taste than most of these trifles of tinted glass were their own ornaments and, in common with all the natives Verrazzano had met, these Indians also disliked the yellow of gold and gilt. They showed a liking for blue and red-colored stones alone, and the little bells charmed them.

"I am not too surprised at their indifference," said Conflans, "for these appear to be superior people."

"Oh, they are." Verrazzano nodded. "Distinctly superior," he said. "That is evident at a glance."

"Giovanni, we have some lengths of silk. Perhaps that would appeal to them."

"We can try it."

A sailor fetched the silks and gave them to Verrazzano. Like a merchant trying to sell his wares, he displayed satins and taffetas. The silks flashed in the sun and trembled in the wind.

Again the Indians smiled and shook their heads.

Verrazzano laughed. "*Va bene,* they are hard to please. I admire them the more for being that way. Captain, somehow we must get to know these people."

Conflans said, "Do you suppose they'd come aboard?"

"Well, suppose we drop the ladder over the side and see."

As soon as this was done, Verrazzano resumed his entreaties.

"Come," he invited. "Come up. Up." He pointed to the ladder, then lifted his hands in an upward motion. "Up. Up," he repeated. Friendliness rang in his voice and radiated from his smile.

The people understood and accepted. Four oarsmen stayed in every canoe—nearly all Indians did things by fours, the number of the winds and the corners of the earth—while their occupants, men, women, and children, followed the two kings up the ladder with a jingle and metallic clink. Men and boys wore leg and arm ornaments fashioned of layers of copper disks, one overlapping the other. With every move of legs and arms the thinly pounded circlets struck one another and clinked. All the way up the Indians laughed and chattered softly, delighting in this incredible experience of scaling a rope ladder to the waistdeck of a big white ship wth square canvas wings, flags, and a multicolored dolphin carved of wood. There were some, however, who neither now nor at any other time were permitted by the kings to visit the *Dauphine.* These were the queens and their ladies. While the others were going aboard, two of the twenty canoes silently pushed off.

The exotic queens and their courts of ladies were rowed to an islet within view.

Greatly attracted to these people, Verrazzano gives us a glimpse of what he saw and thought on this occasion:

There were among these people two kings, handsome men of fine physique and stature ... the one a man of about xxxx years, the other a young man of xxiiii years ... The older one had on the skin of a stag adorned like damask with heavy embroideries; his head was bare, the hair smoothly turned back with a variety of bands; from the neck hung a broad chain lavishly ornamented with stones of different colors. The young man was similarly garbed ... This is the most beautiful and the most civilized people that we found in the entire course of this voyage. In size they excel us; in complexion they differ one from the other. Some are bronze-colored, some incline to fairness, others to a tawny shade. The facial features are sharply cut; the hair is long and black, and they give considerable study to dressing it. The eyes are black and alert, the bearing kind and gentle.

If one wonders whether a man as dedicated to his profession and as preoccupied with a goal as Verrazzano ever had an eye for women, the answer is that he had, provided the women measured up to his criteria. Of these women he wrote:

The women are charming and beautiful; very graceful; of comely mien and most agreeably modest behavior ... They too wear one skin of the stag embroidered like the men's, and some wear on the arms very rich skins of the lynx. The head is bare, the hair dressed in intricate braid arrangements ... Some use hair styles such as the women of Egypt and Syria use, and these are the women who are married or who are advanced in age. From their earlobes hang pendent trinkets like those the Orientals are accustomed to wear. Among the men and women one sees disks and chains made of copper, which they prize above gold. They deem gold worthless because of its yellow color. Blue and red they rate over every other color. That which the women were given by us which they did not return were little bells, and trifles of blue crystals to place in the ears and on the neck ... They show no liking for silk or for cloth of gold. It is the same with metal like steel and iron. The men and women manifested no pleasure at seeing our weapons, and expressed no wish to have them. But all examined the workmanship closely. They did the same thing with the mirrors. After looking at them, they refused them graciously. For their part, they are so liberal that all which they own they willingly give away ... We formed a firm friendship with them.

Prior to a storm, the Indians proved their friendship, not for the first time or the last. Moved by their generosity and concern, Verrazzano makes their solicitude known in this paragraph:

One day, before we had entered with the ship in the port, remaining anchored a league at sea because of uncertain weather conditions, a host of people came in their barges to the ship. As a token to us of their amity they had painted their faces with various colors. They brought to us abundant food, and signaled where, for our safety and the ship's, we should anchor in the port. Then they continually escorted us until we cast anchor there.

Having been guided by the Indians to a place of refuge may account for Verrazzano's choice of a name for this "port of very great beauty." He called it *Porto Refugio*. More than a century later a town was founded on the shores of Porto Refugio by the Englishman, William Coddington. He named it Newport.

All the way from the site of his first landfall to Porto Refugio Verrazzano showed himself to be keenly observant, gathering a quantity of nautical and other information that in time would add to the knowledge of navigators, explorers, and colonizers. Aside from looking for a passage to the South Sea, which he now realized was nowhere in these parts, his voyage was a preliminary exploration with a view to French colonies eventually being established in those areas which seemed to him best suited for this purpose. He took special note of the Indians, their physical stature, skin color, dress, customs, behavior, attitude toward foreigners; similarities and contradictions in the different tribes. Verrazzano the naturalist and dreamer wandered among flowers and vine-hung trees, was reminded of Italy and became homesick. Verrazzano the explorer assayed climates, locations, types of soil, looked for signs of minerals and ores, studied coastlines with future harbors in mind. He was ever on the alert for inlets and coves where ships could be secure in times of storm; for rocks that might endanger ships; for shallow waters and deep. He kept his leadsman busy taking soundings.

The general area of what is known today as North Carolina, Maryland, Virginia, Delaware, and New Jersey lent itself, he believed, to the building of ports, to the cultivation of farms and dairy farms, orchards, vineyards, and flowers. Angoulême offered the perfect site for a focal point of trade and shipping. Porto Refugio, its environs and people, held a high potential for everything profitable and good. Verrazzano sums up its possibilities:

> Many times we walked five or six leagues inland, finding it most pleasing, adapted to every kind of cultivation, particularly grain, wine, and oil ... These people have more system in farming than any others we have met. They mark the full moon, the rising of the Pleaides, and many customs derived from the ancients ... The fields are from xxv to xxx leagues in width, and so fertile that any seed in them would yield excellent crops ... We found Lucullian apples [wild cherries] and plums, and fruits different from ours.

> There are many animals. Stags, deer, lynx, and other species. In the manner of the other people, these also catch them with snares and bows ... The arrows are fashioned with unusual beauty, tipped with jasper, marble, or other sharp stones; not iron. It is with stones, not iron, that they cut down trees for their barges. These are made from a single tree trunk and, with stone, they hollow it

out with marvelous skill. Completed, the barge will
carry xiv or xv persons easily. The oar is short with
a broad end. They work it with the strength of the
arms alone . . . and with as much haste as they wish.

Going farther inland, we saw their dwellings. They
are circular, constructed of limber saplings which
they bend in the shape of an arbor. The habitations
are overlaid with ingeniously woven straw mats
which keep out the wind and rain . . . Beyond a
doubt, if these people were trained in the arts they
would build magnificent structures, for all this maritime coast is rich in blue rocks, crystal, and alabaster. . . .[21]

Apart from being handsome and genial, the people
were highly intelligent, artistic, resourceful, and co-
operative. Verrazzano came to know them well for the
two kings, accompanied by their attendants, visited the
*Dauphine* daily. Nothing, however, that Verrazzano
could say or do sufficed to persuade the kings to bring
their queens on board. He says:

Every day they came to see us, bringing their
women, of whom they were very careful . . . Board-
ing the ship themselves, they made their queens
stay in the barge, and no matter how much we en-
treated, they refused to allow them to enter the
ship.

And one of the two kings coming often with the
queen . . . sent her with her ladies in a barge to stay
on a little island distant from us a quarter of a
league. He himself remained a very long time, dis-
coursing by gestures, examining all the ship's equip-

ment, asking the purpose of everything, tasting our food, and then parting from us benignly.

Wherever Verrazzano and his men, most of whom were Normans, came in contact with the Indians he was watchful as to whether the French temperament was compatible with the Indian, and vice versa, for if the French were to found colonies on these coasts they and the natives would have to live and work and learn together in harmony. So far, mutual friendliness everywhere decided him to urge King Francis to lose no time in sending settlers and all that was needed in order to establish colonies. Aside from farm animals, seeds, grains, and implements of all kinds, he wanted men of every profession. Farmers, millers, smiths, weavers, vintners, teachers, architects, writers, artists, masons, shipbuilders. Priests would find it easy to instill in these people Christian beliefs. About the religion of the natives they had met, Verrazzano made this surmise:

How much religion these peoples have, we were not able to judge, chiefly because of language difficulties. We think they have neither religion nor law, nor know a First Cause or Supreme Being, nor worship the sky, stars, sun, moon, or other planets, nor practice any kind of idolatry, nor make sacrifice . . . nor that their villages have temples or churches for prayer.

We are of the opinion they have not any creed . . . and they are readily persuaded to worship, for all that they saw done by us that had to do with the divine worship they imitated with fervor.

Verrazzano evidently felt that missionaries would be welcome and their presence justified. But he said nothing about a need for physicians. All the indigenes that he met enjoyed wonderfully good health, and none better than those in Porto Refugio. Marveling at their longevity, haleness, and habit of cauterizing cuts and wounds against infection, he provides this bit of information:

> They live to a very great age and are almost never ill. If they wound themselves, without crying they heal themselves by applying fire to the wound. They do not die of disease or illness, only of old age.

Fifteen days in Porto Refugio was time enough for Verrazzano to become attached to the *indigeni,* natives, and they to him. More than any other, this place would remain in his mind like a song that continually recurs, usually in short passages. The passages would tell, for example, of the memory of the winsome, well-behaved little children, and the merriness and warmth in their shining black eyes whenever he patted their heads or their brown-rosy cheeks, or took a small chin in his hand and murmured, *"Dolci, dolci."* To look at him, to know his strictness as a commander, one might not suspect it was in him to say "sweet, sweet" to a child, or that children were drawn to him. But they were, sensing as children do that he was a person of deep sensitivity and personal emotions. Verrazzano was unique in his understanding of youngsters and youths, and he showed especial attention to frightened and homesick young sailors.

Other passages of this song would describe the fields, forests, and waters. And above all the people; their generosity, gentleness, intelligence, loyalty, and engaging dignity stole his heart away completely and revealed what qualities Verrazzano looked for and most admired in human beings. No doubt there were many things that stamped themselves upon his memory, among them the practical lessons that he learned from these people. If he were a settler he would know how to plant corn their way, four grains at a time; how to bake a potful of beans overnight in a pit in the ground where a fire was built; how to make a canoe; how to caulk leaks and cracks in a boat with resinous tree gum; how to enrich and fertilize crops with seaweed; how to keep ears of corn field-fresh and the meat of filbert nuts from drying up by packing both in deep sands.

*May 6.* Quietly a fleet of canoes preceded the *Dauphine.* Two weeks earlier they had formed an escort of welcome. Now it was good-by. As the oarsmen neared the mouth of the port they halted. The *Dauphine* advanced. The moment Verrazzano and Conflans came into view on the poopdeck, the two kings, wearing great collars of copper studded with chunky blue stones, stood up in their boats. The sunlight gleamed upon their bronze-brown bodies and caught the flash of copper.

"What fine, handsome people! I hate to leave them," said Captain Conflans.

Verrazzano nodded and swallowed visibly. Then he

raised his red-sleeved arms and waved repeatedly, saying, "*Addio, amici, addio.*"

In their own language his friends shouted, "Come back to us soon! Come again!"

The *Dauphine* moved ahead, the Indian canoes receded.

Verrazzano had fulfilled the duty he imposed upon himself to baptize coasts, hills, capes, ports, and islands for the royal family of France and for chosen French peers. Now he was as free as the love he need no longer keep confined, love for Italian compatriots and Italy. Name-giving was the only means he had of honoring certain of his friends and his native land. He believed this tribute would endure. It didn't. The names he gave to parts of what today are the United States were blotted out with the arrival of Dutch and English colonists who christened their settlements after their kings, queens, benefactors, towns, and provinces in their own homelands.

Before he left Porto Refugio, Verrazzano gave Italian names to a large rock and a headland. He says:

> Toward the entrance to the port, on one side and on the other are delightful little hills with rivulets, which from the height of the hills to the sea send down cascades of clear water ... In the midst of the mouth is a rock of petra viva [living rock] produced by nature, adapted for the erection of any desired engine or bulwark for its protection. ...

This rock he named *La Petra Viva*. According to his discreetly worded explanation, he called it that not only "on account of the nature of the stone," [22] but *"per la famiglia di una gentildonna,"* for the family of a gentlewoman.[23] Possibly she was a lady he found it hard to forget. Possibly. Whatever else is pure supposition, this much is fact—before marriage, the lady's surname was the equivalent of Petra Viva. She was Maria Caterina de Pierrevive, a noblewoman of Chieri, near Turin, and the wife of Antonio Gondi, a Florentine noble living in France. A close friend of Verrazzano, Gondi was also a contributor to the voyage. Verrazzano plainly held the lady and her family in high regard, for she was the first of his Italian friends whose name he left on American shores. The cape situated *"a destra della boca del Porto del Refugio,"* at the right side of the mouth of the Port of Refuge, became *Jovium Promontorium* (Promontorio Giovio) for his friend Paolo Cardinal Giovio.

From now on Verrazzano scattered sonorous Italian names over New World areas the way a bird scatters song-notes. After he returned to Europe he provided Maggiolo with new information for Maggiolo's World Map and with a roster of names not recorded in the Cellere Codex.[24] Maggiolo, who was burdened with the impressive office and title of "Chief Navigational Cartographer of the Republic of Genoa," not only added onto his map the names desired by Verrazzano (as well as his own), but also saw his map attain immense value because it reflected Verrazzano's decision as to the relationship between America and Asia. For the first time America was represented on a map as a continent isolated from Asia. For the first time, too, a part of the North American continent was designated *Francesca,*

Verrazzano's name for it, marked by a small French flag patterned with three golden fleurs-de-lis. Two years later, Girolamo da Verrazzano included thirty-five of the names on Maggiolo's map on his own map of the world. But he made one exception. He changed the name *Francesca* to *Verrazana*.[25]

Under sail once again, Verrazzano and Captain Conflans followed the shore and followed their habit of never going out of sight of land while exploring. Leagues later, 150 leagues by their reckoning, fog drew over the sea and over the *Dauphine*. Rain came in cold stinging spurts. Quick to sense and feel changes in the ocean, Verrazzano knew they were in for more than a spell of ugly weather. He expected trouble, but he had no idea as to the nature of it. Anxious, he went with the leadsman at half-hour intervals to take soundings fore and aft, and all round the ship.

"Cast," said Verrazzano.

The leadsman heaved the sounding line. Weighted with lead, the end of the line was coated with wax. After each casting he called out the water's depth.

"Eight fathoms, monsieur." Then, "Six fathoms."

Within an hour the rain let up. Eddies of wind carried away the mist. Pale light touched creamy fringes of foam, touched dunes and shores. The light brightened gradually and enabled Verrazzano to see a headland. Then and there he named it for his friend, General Gian Lodovico Pallavicino. This name, too, would disappear like footprints in the sands. In 1602 Bartholomew Gosnold saw *Promontorio Pallavicino* from his

ship, the *Concord,* and called it Cape Cod, the name
it has retained.

Breakers pushed, retreated, collected, charged forward, and pummeled the *Dauphine.*

"Cast!"

"Four fathoms, monsieur."

Verrazzano felt growing concern and wanted soundings every quarter-hour. When the measure was one
fathom, he said, "Impossible! We are too far offshore
to be in six feet of water. Cast again."

The leadsman cast, then brought up the line. Verrazzano watched him in silence, his face fixed as if in
stone, staring, waiting. "Well?"

"One fathom less a half, monsieur. Sand bottom."

"It can't be."

"Monsieur, *regarde.*" Look. He showed Verrazzano
sand adhering to the wax.

The *Dauphine* was ensnared in the perilous shoals of
Cape Cod, trapped on a sand bank "upon which," wrote
Verrazzano, "there was three feet of water." Only a
navigator of Verrazzano's skill, patience, and calm could
have succeeded in dislodging the vessel without dam-
age to her hull. Even so, in his words, "*passamo con
difficultà,*" we got through it with difficulty.

His ship riding deep water once more, Verrazzano
relaxed and hit upon a name for the shoals that he realized were as treacherous and engulfing as quicksands.
He called them *Sirti d' Armellini,* Armellini being the
plural form of a surname. The surname belonged to
Francesco Armellino, Cardinal of Perugia and papal
treasurer under the Medici pope, Clement VII, nephew

of an earlier pope, Leo X, who was a lover of art and a lavish spender.

Leo X had emptied the papal purse. Armellino filled it by slapping a tax on everything. Hunters and farmers were even taxed for the thrushes they caught for thrush pie, a delicacy. Thrush money alone netted the papacy 2500 golden ducats annually. "If he knew a way to do it," related the Venetian Ambassador, Marco Foscari, "Cardinal Armellino would make flies pay rent and ants pay a tax on the crumbs they carry." Instead, the cardinal tormented the bankers of Rome, excepting two great banking families, the Strozzi and the Chigi. Agostino Chigi often had served Leo X rare foods on plates of gold in stables decorated by Raphael. Then, to the music of fifes and lutes, the golden dishes were thrown into the Tiber, the host wishing to prove that he had no need to use them twice. Other bankers, primarily those who were anti-Medici, were Cardinal Armellino's favorite targets. Among these were the Rucellai and Verrazzani. Bernardo da Verrazzano had felt and was still feeling the pinch. Tongue in cheek, Verrazzano avenged his elder brother by naming the worst spot he came upon in his voyage for the cardinal who plagued Bernardo and his partner, Buonacorso Rucellai.

Disagreeable encounters followed the experience off Cape Cod. This is Verrazzano's report:

> In the space of fifty leagues, holding more to the north, we found a high land full of forests of pines, firs, and trees such as grow in cold regions. The people are different from the others ... They are uncouth, vicious, and so barbarous that despite our

efforts we were never able to communicate with them . . . They wear the skins of bears, lynxes, and other animals . . . They do not have pulse, and we saw no signs of cultivated land . . . The soil is sterile and would not produce fruit or any grain. . . .

When they wished to barter with us they came to the shore and stood upon a steep rock, while we remained in the small boat beneath. Then with a cord they let down to us what they wished to give, continually yelling on land that we should not approach. They dealt with us quickly and refused anything in exchange except knives, fish hooks, and sharp metal. . . .

Contrary to their demands, xxv armed men of us went inland two or three leagues, and when we returned to the shore they shot at us with their bows, sending up a great cry, and then fled into the woods. We did not find anything of value here except the forests, with some hills which possibly have some metal, for many of the natives wore copper beads in their ears.

Without regret, Verrazzano took his leave of *La Terra di Mala Gente,* The Land of Bad People. Skirting the coast "between east and north," he found it "very beautiful, open and bare of forests, with high mountains back inland. . . ." After logging another fifty leagues, the *Dauphine* reached a land of islands. Having found a group of "xxxii" islands, Verrazzano named the three largest The Three Daughters of Navarre. All these islands were small and lovely and "followed the curving of the land" in a way that reminded Verrazzano of the

Adriatic Gulf and of Dalmatia. This Dalmatia of America eventually became the state of Maine.

The natives, similar to the others, had no regard for courtesy. This discouraged Verrazzano and his men from any desire to remain a while among them. Besides, they had consumed most of their "naval stores" in the course of exploring "600 leagues and more of new land." Providing themselves with water and wood, Verrazzano navigated *"intra Subsolano e Aquilone,"* between east-south-east and north-north-west, and after sailing as far "as the land which the Britons found in the past, which stands in 50 degrees North Latitude," he set the course for France, taking the sea-track familiar to Norman and Breton fishermen.

Verrazzano turned the *Dauphine's* prow toward France, and his mind toward Cathay. His ideal was as fixed as ever, his intention unchanged, and he stated it clearly:

> My intention in this navigation was to reach Cathay and the extreme east of Asia, not expecting to find such an obstacle of new land as I found; and if for some reason I expected to find it, I thought it to be not without a strait to penetrate to the Oriental Sea ... This has been the opinion of all the ancients ... and according to experience is untrue. ...

It was still his intention to reach Cathay. But when he set forth again, which he felt certain would be soon, he would go southward toward Darien.[26] His spirit bolstered with this thought, Verrazzano sailed confidently to France, unaware of what awaited him.

# 6

THE SUN was not yet risen. But Verrazzano was up and sitting at his writing table. He lit a candle and sharpened several pens. His libretto and the rough draft of a letter lay within reach of his right hand. At his left was a tooled leather box that held fine Florentine paper, creamy-smooth as magnolia petals. Paper fit for a king. He pulled out a sheet and, culling items from the libretto and outline letter, he began to compose a detailed account of his voyage for his Most Christian Majesty Francis I, King of France.

Verrazzano was writing rapidly when he paused, aware of two differences. Sea-scented air had changed to odors of river water and land, and the *Dauphine* was sliding along as evenly as a gondola in Venice. She was out of the ocean and riding the Seine, a river of many turnings. Halfway down a second sheet of paper Verrazzano noticed that sunshine brightened the cabin with light of a peeled apricot tint. He snuffed the candle's flame and continued his relation of where he had been, what he had seen, what he had done, and what, with the king's aid, he hoped yet to do, not in months or a year from now but soon, very soon. Engrossed, he did not heed the passing of time.

Then all at once a happy sailor on a deck caused Verrazzano to look up with a start and listen, as the sailor shouted, *"Nous sommes en vue de Dieppe!"* We are in view of Dieppe.

With a jolt and a pang Verrazzano realized that the voyage was over. Now he could hear Captain Conflans directing the helmsman; he heard the metallic rattle of anchor chains, excited talk of men, hurried footsteps on the decks and in the gangways, and finally the sound of the gangplank being lowered.

On shore, seamen, dock workers and fishermen let out a cry, "The *Dauphine!* The *Dauphine* is home from Cathay!"

In no time, church bells started up a hasty clanging. Townsfolk came running, crowded the quay. Everybody was thankful, elated. It was many a day since Dieppois had had good news of any kind.

France was under a cloud. King Francis had lost Milan to Emperor Charles V of Spain. In retaliation for what he deemed abuses dealt him by his king, the French Duke of Bourbon deserted Francis and allied himself with Charles, inducing a number of French courtiers to follow him. For Charles the Duke of Bourbon invaded Provence and subdued it in flames. At any moment English armies were expected in Picardy. Francis was preparing a massive counterattack to retake Milan, to retake all Lombardy, a large area in northern Italy, from the increasingly victorious Charles.

But now! What was Milan, what was Provence, what

was Picardy, what was anything compared to a route to Cathay!

Dieppois were wild with joy. Then—bitter disappointment. The Florentine navigator, they learned, had not found a route to Cathay. The *Dauphine's* hold was empty of Eastern cargo.

"Did he bring back anything?" asked a spokesman for the mob.

A sailor said, "Yes. He brought some herbs, some blue and maroon-red Indian corn, and some samples of stone."

"*Juste ciel!* Good heavens, that's all? He left Dieppe thirteen months ago, and weeds, corn, and rocks are all that he has to show for it?"

"There is more, monsieur. The commander has a libretto packed with information, a mind that is kindled with possibilities, plans for French colonies, and plans for another voyage."

"Bah! That kind of cargo is as useless as wet gunpowder. We need a trade route to the Orient. We need marketable goods. This voyage turned out to be a false rainbow."

Downcast and disgusted, most of the people returned to their chores. Relatives of mariners on the *Dauphine* waited around on the quay. Most of the *Dauphine's* men soon disembarked. A dozen remained to take care of odds and ends. On the quay, Conflans was talking with one of Ango's captains. Presently he went back on board, went to Verrazzano's cabin.

The commander had heard the derision, the loud utterances of vexation and sarcasm. He brooded on it all, staring into space. He was hurt, yet stately even in his hurt.

Conflans drew up a chair and sat down. In Brittany he had apologized for the rudeness of the malcontents. Now in Dieppe he apologized for the sudden surliness of the people. "They do not," he said, "comprehend the scope and potentials of the voyage."

"Of course they don't, monsieur. I wouldn't expect them to." Verrazzano excused them, just as Conflans knew he would. "I do not blame them, monsieur. After all, they counted on receiving exactly what I counted on bringing to them. Bales of silk and other fabrics. Thread of gold and silver, thread of many colors. Gems. Gold. Rose attar and musk. Cinnamon, cloves, and pepper. Aromatic gums. Drugs. Lacquers. Rosewood, teakwood, ebony, and ivory. In short, a Far Eastern bazaar in the ship's hold. I was sure. Too sure. What I promised and what I brought are as different as rubies and red corn. The people feel cheated and deceived. I am sorriest about that."

Conflans knew this last to be an understatement. He could see that the attitude of the people was a crushing weight on Verrazzano's mind and heart.

There was a silence.

From outside came the stir and laughter of sailors, the cry of fishmongers, the rhythmic tlup—tlup—tlup— tlup of water washing the *Dauphine's* sides. Gulls wheeled around her masts, whimpering like wounded dogs. Even the birds, it seemed to Verrazzano, were whining complaints about him.

"Though thwarted of my goal, monsieur, I do not

despair of attaining it. I failed, but I am not defeated. I shall find a road to Cathay, and soon."

Conflans nodded without speaking. Then he said, "Don't pin your hopes on going very soon. France is at war in her own country and in yours." Conflans gave him all the news he'd had from the captain on the quay. At first he thought Verrazzano had not listened, for it took a long moment before the fact of war in Italy reached him. Then a startled, pained look crossed his face. Any mention of Italy invariably roused some inner yearning in Verrazzano. It was then that the hidden things of the heart showed in his eyes, and the stern look softened.

Changing the subject, Conflans said, "The captain told me that Ango is at his summer place. Next week he will be in Dieppe for a day or so. Shall you go to Varengeville to see him or wait until he comes here?"

"I'll wait. Why dishearten him sooner than I have to?"

"Ango isn't easily disheartened. He will be disappointed, but not for long. He is certain to appreciate what you accomplished."

"I didn't accomplish what I set out to do."

"No, but you, like Columbus on his first voyage, found what you were not looking for."

"It's true enough that I found a hindrance I did not anticipate."

"That is not what I mean. Giovanni, you found another world in the New World. Different. Unusual. Cathay is an old story. Your land of Francesca is a new one."

"But I did not find a way to the Orient, and that is what I was commissioned to do."

"Look, at this point, in this mood, can you judge whether what you found is less important than what you sought?"

"No, I cannot. I can see immense possibilities and gains. Yet these cannot be realized save by means which now are not to be considered. France needs men and money for wars. She is in no position to send people to colonize, cultivate, teach, and enhance with French culture a land across the Atlantic. It is tragic that the ambitions and threats of Charles V, and the vindictiveness of Bourbon, prevent the French from going to Francesca. Then again I suppose it is wiser to first obtain greater knowledge of the interior of the lands we coasted. This I mean to do, after I find an entry to the South Sea."

"Immediate royal sanction for a second voyage isn't likely, Giovanni."

"I am armored with patience, monsieur."

Captain Conflans drew his grayish brows together in thought, then smiled and urged Verrazzano to go ashore and take a meal with him.

"Thank you, monsieur. You are gracious. Will another day do? I have a letter to write to the king."

"Of course."

Conflans stood up. Verrazzano stood up. Each gave the other a concentrated gaze. This was probably their last moment together, and they knew it. Conflans was in constant demand to examine ships of all nations, including Egypt and Syria. Within a matter of days he was apt to be off to a foreign country. Verrazzano wanted to tell him all he was not able to say: his admiration for his skill and learning; gratitude for his companionship and kindness; all the warmth of his feeling for him. But for this there were no words. He smiled. The smile was pensive. The dark eyes were pensive, infinitely sad.

"Adieu, mon capitaine."

A note of forlornness in Verrazzano's words and voice caused Conflans' forced firmness to weaken, and his voice broke. Quickly he left the young nobleman who was ever solicitous of him, especially during the storms, mindful of him at all times with an almost filial esteem and devotion.

Verrazzano looked at the open, empty doorway. Farewells were painful. The previous night he had spoken a few words of farewell to the crew. Now Conflans had left. Loneliness pervaded Verrazzano. He returned to his chair and drugged himself with work in order to dull the ache inside him.

A sailor slipped in at midday, set a tray on the table, and tried to tempt Verrazzano with filet de sole Normande, salad, crusty bread, fruit, wine, and creamy Norman cheese. An hour later he removed the tray. The food was untouched. In another hour or so Verrazzano finished the letter. He was signing it when the same seaman who had taken away the tray appeared at the door and said, "Mon commandant, a gentleman to see you."

Verrazzano turned, got up, and was greeted by a Norman friend [1] whose cordiality bewildered him. Acutely conscious of the hostile feeling toward him now, he was astonished that any Frenchman was pleased to see him. Was it possible that his visitor was uninformed as to the outcome of the voyage? To make sure that he was not, Verrazzano said to him, "I failed, you know."

"That is what the people say, Giovanni. Tell me, do you still believe in your goal and in your motive for pursuing it?"

"I do, yes. Implicitly."

"Then you have not failed. In matters of this kind the average man cannot see beyond his nose. His gaze is outward. Yours is inward. The man who believes in something extraordinary generally finds himself separated from those who don't by an invisible wall that is colder and higher than the Alps."

"Nevertheless," said Verrazzano, "philosophizing about it does not stock a tradesman's shelves. From their side of the wall the people's anger is justified. They have to think of the practical side of life."

"*Alors*, why are you still on board, Giovanni?"

"I have work to do."

"You look tired."

"I am."

"Come to my place. You need to relax."

"Thank you, not just yet."

"Is there something I can do?"

Verrazzano gave this thought. His friend liked to write and he had not only a clear and elegant script but an admirable command of Italian as well. "I will appreciate your help," Verrazzano said, "if you have time to spare."

"I have the whole day."

"What I want shouldn't take all that long."

"*Bon,* what is it you want me to do?"

"Take down a letter as I tell it to you. My whole hand," said Verrazzano as he flexed his fingers, "aches from having gripped a pen since before daybreak."

"Gladly, Giovanni. I'll write as many letters as it pleases you to dictate."

Verrazzano was to dictate several letters, communications destined for his family and close friends.[2] Each letter was patterned on the Letter to the King, practically the same in content but varied in length and wording. And even though only one letter was dictated now, and the others later, all bore the same ending as that given in the letter to Francis I, and also the same date, the day of Verrazzano's return to Dieppe.

Fruit and wine were brought to the cabin to sustain the scribe. The afternoon passed. Finally, like its model, the duplicate letter ended with these words:

*Ne la nave Delfina a di viii Luglio M. D. XXIIII.*
*Humilis servitor Janus Verazanus.*

In the ship *Dauphine,* July 8, 1524.[3] Humble servant Janus Verazanus.

Documents signed by Verrazzano in France carry a Latinized form of his family name. No rule prevails for Latinizing surnames, so we find "Verazanus," "Verrazanus," and, in Paolo Giovio's *Elogia Virorum,* "Verazanius." Inconsistencies abound in the Latinizing of names. One example appears in a contract discussed by

Bacchiani and Hall in their Introduction to the Cellere Codex. The contract was drawn up by Giulio de Alberini for Bernardo da Verrazzano and Buonacorso di Rucellai, members of closely allied Florentine families. The two banking partners leased for nine years the grand Palazzo Alberini in Rome's Via Banco di Santo Spirito. In part, the contract reads:

> *Julius Alberinis* . . . has leased and rented to Lord *Bernardus de Verazano* and *Bonacurious de Oricelariis,* the house of himself. . . . [italics added]

Scarcely less puzzling than these and other Latin oddities was Giovanni da Verrazzano's habit of signing himself *Janus* in letters and legal papers. A Latinist who scattered Latinisms throughout his letter of the voyage of 1524, he knew well enough that Janus is not the Latin form of Giovanni (John). It is not a Latin name at all. Steeped in mythology—a characteristic of many Florentine Renaissance scholars—he undoubtedly was familiar with Janus, the Roman deity-guardian of gates and doors. In his desire to fling open the gates of the Orient to France, it is possible that he responded to the symbolism in the name, especially since he seems not to have used it except in France. Also, the euphony in the two names must have appealed to his ear and his poetic fancy, for *Janus Verazanus* is a heroic sculpture of a name worked of the substance of rich soft sounds.

Verrazzano was eager to have this first dictated letter written and dispatched without delay. The work being completed, he dismissed his scribe with bountiful thanks and agreed to meet with him the next day or the day after next. Alone once more, he scanned the twelve numbered sheets, and suddenly remembered items that were in the Letter to the King but which he had failed to include in this one. He now wrote annotations in the margins and in between the lines. Unlike the smooth, round-handed courtscript of his copyist, Verrazzano wrote in a nervous, angular hand. In the twenty-six hurriedly written additions, erasures, ink spots, and stricken out words betrayed his weariness.

The blots, corrections, and nearly illegible writing did not, however, detract from the letter's worth. On the contrary, they made its value immense. A number of the annotations concern the naming of places and the reasons for the names, specifically Annunziata, Arcadia, Angoulême, the Bay of Santa Margherita, and Isola Aloysia. One lengthy annotation has to do with the "oriental sea" and the strip of land that presented a barrier to reaching it.

The twenty-six inclusions did much more than provide the reader with names, localities, and brief descriptions. When this letter was rediscovered, after 385 years, it was the annotations that settled once and for all the truth of a long doubted fact, doubted by some historians, and the absolute falseness of an idea that these and other historians accepted as indisputable fact. Without ever knowing that he needed to prove he had made a voyage to America, or needed to prove that he was Giovanni da Verrazzano, not "Juan Florin, the French pirate," he unwittingly cleared up both matters by messing up the beautiful manuscript with sprawling notations. When the letter was found, in the twentieth century, handwriting experts established beyond a doubt that the marginal notes and interlinear comments and corrections were written by the same Janus Verazanus whose writing appears on a document which is preserved in the Archives of the Normandy Parliament at Rouen.[4]

Apart from the lost Letter to the King, this is the only known letter about Verrazzano's voyage of 1524 which is amply covered with his own penmanship. At the bottom of the verso of the eleventh sheet he wrote:

*A Leonardo Tedaldi o a Thomaso Sartini, mercanti in Leone. Mandaretelo a Bonacorso Rucellai.*

Tedaldi and Sartini were Florentine noblemen in Lyons. Sartini was a banker. Verrazzano addressed the letter to one or the other and directed either one to forward the letter to Bernardo da Verrazzano's banking associate, Buonarcorso di Rucellai. These three friends, as well as Verrazzano's brother, were among those who had financed the voyage. He was naturally anxious to send word to them as soon as possible. It is certain that when he addressed this letter it never entered his mind that the document, intended for intimate friends, would go back to "Angoulême" some 400 years later, and that it would be priceless and be known variously as the Giovio and the Cellere Codex.

It was suddenly very quiet. The *Dauphine's* men, he supposed, had all gone ashore. He was and yet was not surprised when someone rapped on the open door and said, "Mon commandant?"

He recognized the voice. "*Entre, entre,* Matelot," he said. "Come in. I thought I was quite alone."

"No, monsieur. I am here," The blond, blue-eyed sailor entered the cabin and placed on the table what looked to be nothing more than a piece of cloth intricately folded.

"Thank you, Matelot. Thank you for remembering."

The sailor regarded Verrazzano unhappily. The usual vitality in the handsome face, the leonine strength in the lean frame, were overlaid with bodily and emotional fatigue. "Monsieur, it is late."

"Is it?"

"Yes, monsieur. The sun is going down."

Verrazzano smiled reflectively. "Once, Matelot, you said to me, 'What a sunrise we shall see in Cathay!' I am sorry that we did not see it there."

"It's all right, monsieur. We saw wonderful sunrises in *La Francescane.*"

"No, it is not all right," Verrazzano said, and lapsed into silence. It was as if he were trying to understand why they had not reached Cathay, but his thoughts strayed and became confused.

"Shall I wait, monsieur?"

"Wait? What for?"

"For you, monsieur."

"Oh. No. No, thank you."

"Are you sure?"

"Yes, I am sure. You ought to have gone ashore hours ago."

The youth hesitated. He opened his mouth, but no sound came. All he could do was gaze at his commander with a sad expression. Verrazzano felt the look, got to his feet and held out his hand to this devoted young Norman.

"Adieu, Matelot," he said. "Adieu et merci."

"Adieu, mon commandant." Like Captain Conflans before him, the sailor left Verrazzano unwillingly, yet in haste. His were the last footsteps that Verrazzano would hear on the *Dauphine*, the last except his own.

Clothing, books, armor, navigational instruments, charts, and other belongings had been taken to his lodgings. He locked the letters and libretto inside a leather wallet, passed the shoulder strap over his head and adjusted the buckle. He put on his velvet beret and again his eyes touched slowly every corner of the cabin. Carefully he took up what the sailor had brought to him, stood in lonely silence for a moment longer, then left the cabin and closed the door behind him.

He went for a last stroll on the poop. Afar, the chalk white cliffs were spectral in the lavender dusk. In the harbor, lanterns on galiots and fishing boats twinkled like stars drifted to the water. Only the *Dauphine* was dark. Verrazzano looked up at her bare spars. Her sails were down. Reluctant to leave, he put the moment off as long as possible. Finally, he went ashore.

Slowly he walked a distance on the cobbled quay, then came to a standstill and looked back. Gallant little *Dauphine!* Verrazzano loved her in much the way that Christopher Columbus had loved the *Niña*, the smallest and bravest of any caravel he ever sailed. Emotion caught at Verrazzano's throat and brimmed in his eyes. Choking with unspoken words and stifled feelings, Giovanni da Verrazzano turned away from the ship of his first voyage to America, a valiant little ship that deserves a place in American history.

Adieu. Adieu. The word seemed to crash against his heart. He clutched to his breast a token of the voyage and a symbol of home. His flag. The proud flag of proud Florence. Out into the deepening dusk he walked. A sad man, a lonely man, but a hopeful man, of great heart. How long must he wait, he wondered, before he would achieve something for the good of others? How long before his flag would ripple from a ship's mast again?

# 7

◈◈◈ Fragrance of boxwood and yellow jasmine drifted on the hot wind from the patio to the room in the Seville Alcázar where Peter Martyr was writing a letter. *Epistle DCCC* concerned "Florin the French pirate." Florin, related Peter Martyr, had just attacked a Portuguese galleon en route to Lisbon from the East Indies, and had taken to La Rochelle cargo valued at "almost 200,000 ducats." Writing in an atmosphere of beauty, this scholar who was dedicated to justice was entirely innocent of the ugliness and injustice that would stem from this letter, which was dated August 3, 1524.

Three and a half centuries later, a book [1] was published in New York in which, despite printed proof to the contrary, Giovanni da Verrazzano was defamed as "Juan Florin the pirate." The author used Peter Martyr's Epistle 800 to bolster this conviction and to support his erroneous belief that Verrazzano was a villainous adventurer without morals or conscience, and an ill-bred pirate who exulted over a voyage to North America which, according to the author, he never made. Referring to Epistle 800, he argued that "Juan Florin" could not have been in America in 1524 and at the same time have stolen cargo in Portuguese waters. His reasoning was right but his accusation was wrong. The pirate who pillaged the East Indian cargo was Jean Fleury, whose name is absent in the American author's book. Not yet a month returned from his voyage, Verrazzano was in Dieppe, preparing to visit friends in Lyons.

With exceptions, Ango among them, Dieppois now distrusted and ignored Verrazzano. Jean Fleury, on the other hand, was hailed in La Rochelle with relief and rejoicing, although the rejoicing was restrained in deference to the recent death of Queen Claude.

On August 4, 1524, one day after Epistle 800 was written, Bernardo Carli, a Florentine in Lyons, wrote to his father in Florence about the voyage of Giovanni da Verrazzano *"nostro fiorentino,"* [2] our Florentine. If some Dieppois belittled Verrazzano and his seemingly worthless enterprise, Carli made it plain in his letter that Verrazzano's compatriots in France regarded him as heroic. They considered him the equal of Amerigo Vespucci. He had, wrote Carli, "displayed noble and very great courage in undertaking such an unknown voyage with only one ship and only fifty men ... with the intention, if possible, of reaching Cathay." Captain Verrazzano was eagerly awaited in Lyons and ought, said Carli, "to be here at this very hour." Carli spoke for all the Italians in Lyons when he expressed the hope that Verrazzano would have a chance to converse with the king, who was expected in Lyons within a few days. "And," he wrote, "we all hope that his Serene Majesty

will entrust him again with half a dozen good ships and
that he will return to the voyage . . . and we hope that
he may discover profitable matter . . . and will, our Lord
granting him life, do honor to our country [Italy] in
acquiring immortal fame and memory."

Fervent hopes, theirs and Verrazzano's. But they now
stood no chance of fulfillment. War intervened. Combat
between France and Spain in Italy was no more to be
halted than are the seasons in their course.

Time passed. Summer's green turned into orangy-
gold. October's paths were carpeted with leaves as dead
as leafage painted on a canvas. Late autumn's winds
swept across them like brooms. Then came winter's
rains and sleety gusts, bare trees and seas peaked with
foam.

After visits to friends in Lyons and Rouen, Verrazzano returned to Dieppe and was assailed by restless-
ness. He tortured himself with a feeling of failure.
*Francesca* haunted him. It, too, was a failure, an abandoned enterprise. His lonely hours were filled with
thoughts of home, with the disaster that had again
befallen oft-invaded Italy. His heart was ever in Italy.
The rest of himself he leased temporarily to France. His
nostalgia abated somewhat when his youngest brother
joined him in Dieppe. Girolamo was nearest to him
in age and closest in shared interests. A capable navigator, he preferred the career of cartographer. Devoted
brothers, they were both alike and unlike. Giovanni felt
things intensely but veiled his emotions in a typical
Florentine guise of aloofness. Girolamo openly showed
his feelings. No fixed idea motivated by humanistic

ideals tormented Girolamo. He was lighter of heart than Giovanni, yet readily given to apprehensive hunches and worry. Though serious, his hazel eyes had neither the darkness nor the inscrutable sadness that characterized Giovanni's eyes and, once seen, made them unforgettable. Nor did he have the lost, dreamy look that so often gentled Giovanni's look of sternness. At this difficult time of waiting, Girolamo's presence animated his brother the way a beam of sunshine penetrates a cloud.

Toward the end of 1524 heartening news arrived in Lyons, where Louise of Savoy, queen regent in the king's absence, had her court. Francis had pried Milan loose from the tight fist of Charles V. Hopes soared for a hasty end to the war.

Then, early in 1525, Charles' imperial troops—he himself was in Spain—met Francis I leading his army of Frenchmen, loyal Italians, and hired Swiss pikemen. The two armies confronted one another in Pavia, a suburb of Milan. Spain's officers chose for the field of battle a large area near the *Certosa,* a Carthusian monastery so palatial and fantastic in design that Merlin might have built it, not the dukes of Milan who asked no better reward than to be entombed in the ornate monastery church. After a brash blare of trumpets and the rattle of drums, the battle was on. Two hours later, one wall of the Certosa was in ruins and the blood of 10,000 slain men oozed into the ancient soil of Pavia.

A lifeless horse lay atop its fallen rider. The stunned warrior's gold-washed helmet shone with a cluster of rubies as with a huge red-gleaming eye, and a white plume lifted a little in the ill-smelling wind. He lay, it seemed, upon a bright blue pavement. A group of Charles' mercenaries saw him, his helplessness, the helmet, and the blue mantle with its scattered flashings of silvery-white lilies embroidered upon it.

"It is he! It is he!" they cried. "Quick! Let us kill him! What a trophy!"

The horse with its heavy battle trappings offered a hindrance.

"Drag it off!"

Several halberdiers proceeded to remove the rigid mount. Others stripped the wounded man of breastplate and gorget, snatched off his neckchain, and his baldric belt all stitched with jewels.

"The helmet! The golden helmet is mine!"

With a maniacal shout of triumph, one of the ruffians cocked the helmet with rubies and plume upon his own head. The shout struck the ears of Captain Pomperant. He saw the halberdier and saw the golden casque. Only one man in France wore a clump of rubies and a white panache on his battle hat. Pomperant screamed to them, "Don't touch him! Drop that chain, belt, and helmet, or hang for it!" He then called for Charles de Lannoy, raced to the struggling man and rescued him.

Face bleeding, left hand streaming blood, the king of France was helped to his feet by Pomperant and de Lannoy, both followers of Bourbon. To the dirge of Gascon bagpipes and wail of trumpets, they led the conquered king into the monastery church through a cannon breach in the wall. Here his wounds were cleansed and dressed. The two who had betrayed him

had also saved his life. Francis thanked them and accepted their homage. Anxious now to serve him, they
asked to know his wants. At this moment his wants
were few. He asked merely for pen, ink, and paper.

A portable writing box was brought. Francis fingered
the pen and gazed about him at the tombs of the lords
of Milan. Each in turn, like himself, had been victor
and victim. Finally, in this overadorned burial church
of Milanese rulers, the ruler of France wrote to his
mother. For France the outcome of the Battle of Pavia
was calamitous. The king put it in six memorable
words:

> *Madame, tout est perdu fors l'honneur.*
> Madame, all is lost except honor.

The short but brutal Battle of Pavia occurred on
February 24, 1525, the twenty-fifth birthday of Charles
V. His Spanish commander at Pavia, Antonio de Leyva,
found it as easy to write at length of conquest to
Charles as Francis found it painful to tell his mother
in six words that all was lost except honor. The same
courier, Captain Peñalosa, who carried in his wallet de
Leyva's letter of victory to Charles V, went first to
Lyons to deliver to the queen regent that crushing mas-
terpiece of brevity written by Francis I to his mother.

This done, Francis, with a sudden cold withdrawal,
stood up, gathered his blood-splotched mantle about
him, and waited for what he knew was to come. It approached him in the persons of Spanish nobles and
French nobles in the service of Spain. Impressed by the
king's dignity in the face of defeat, they performed

their duty with as much reluctance as courtesy. By command, not choice, they took the king of France prisoner, and with him those of his nobles who had survived the savagery at Pavia.[3]

Most of the young aristocracy of France lay dead in Pavia. At their sides lay fallen Italian lords who had fought with the French in the endeavor to save Italy from the domination of Charles V. The Battle of Pavia took from Giovanni and Girolamo da Verrazzano two compatriots and friends, General Pallavicino and the Grand Equerry of France, Galeazzo di Sanseverino. Verrazzano had given the General's name to a cape (Promontorio Pallavicino). He now added for future inclusion on maps the name of Sanseverino, a model of Italian knighthood. The slaying at Pavia of Admiral Bonnivet had Francis I grieving for a jaunty but loyal courtier, and Verrazzano for a benefactor who had readily approved the voyage of 1524 and whose approval he had counted on again.

The future was a fog with scarcely a star-point of hope glimmering behind it. France mourned. France raged when word arrived that the king and his counselors were prisoners of war. King and nobles had been shipped to Spain. Housed in the Madrid Alcázar, they were treated in a manner befitting their rank, but the atmosphere nevertheless was tense. Charles and Francis greeted one another with a show of amity, but rancor festered beneath the surface cordiality.

Meanwhile, France had no king and no admiral. Verrazzano, who had said he was armored with patience, discovered chinks in the armor. Not easily, he resisted his brother's urging that they go home. Instead, he resolved to wait for the king's return and the appointment of a new admiral. While he waited he charted a new voyage and worked at calculations and costs with a feverish intensity that was alien to his coolly pensive manner. For him, work alone filled the yawning gap of time.

Rather than narrow, the gap seemed to widen. Often accused of being inconsistent, King Francis consistently rejected the peace terms. Matters had reached an impasse, for Charles was adamant in his demands and Francis defied them. Day after day, Spanish, Flemish, and German officials in Charles' entourage would go to Francis, treaty in hand, set it before him and advise him to sign. And day after day he refused to declare himself ready to accept the demands embodied in the Treaty of Madrid.

The officials complained to the Emperor. "The king of France is obstinate. He will not sign." In turn, Charles complained to the Duke of Alba. "Francis is headstrong," he said. "I offer peace. He spurns it. What can I do?"

"The terms are too lenient, sire. Make them harsher."

Charles abided by the duke's suggestion. The demands were increased and made more humiliating, more ruinous to Francis than before.[4]

Sign. Sign. Sign. Sign. The word repeated itself in the king's brain like the incessant ticking of the emperor's collection of clocks. As time passed, Francis, miserable and ill, merely shook his head when urged to sign. Alarmed by his prisoner's pallor and inertia, Charles sent his physicians to prescribe for the king.

"Our remedies are to no purpose, sire. Without freedom on honorable terms, the king would rather die. He has lost the will to live."

Frantic, Charles shouted at the doctors. "If he dies, I will be blamed. People will say that I had him poisoned. Do something! Do something before it is too late!"

"Majesty, you alone can restore the king to health. Give him his freedom."

"No."

"Sign, Francis."

"No. Sooner than sign the Treaty of Madrid I will abdicate my throne."

This news reached France as swiftly and with as much sting as if it had been carried on the cold, icicle-sharp winds that blew from Madrid's Guadarrama mountains. It threw France into a state of shock. Monarchs and scholars deplored the emperor's excessive demands and his harassment of Francis. A subject of the emperor, the Dutch humanist, Erasmus, went in person to beg Charles to free the king of France and not require him to yield to terms disastrous to himself and to his nation. Erasmus pleaded eloquently, but it availed him nothing. Unheeded, he left Madrid toward the year's end. Then, like a blood-red setting sun the embattled year of 1525 sank into history.

Francis began again to resist total defeat. Heartening for France was this change of mood and mind in the king. Verrazzano found himself smiling, found himself laying his plans for another voyage before Jean d'Ango. His eyes shone with relief when Ango did not reject the plans. The voyage, however, could not be authorized until after Francis returned and named a new admiral. There was nothing for it but to wait.

In Madrid, Francis seemed about to submit, and Charles fell to pondering. He wondered: If Francis signs, will he sign in good faith? Will he give me Burgundy and most of eastern France? Will he stay out of Italy? Will he pardon Bourbon? Will he furnish troops to escort me to Rome for my second coronation? Will he provide money for the festivities? Will he marry my sister Eleanor? If he fails to honor these or other articles in the treaty he is obliged to surrender himself as my prisoner. Can I trust him to do that?

King Francis also had a matter to ponder. At last he said to his counselors, "Is a signature given under duress and torment valid?"

"Sire, it is not."

Without more ado, Francis I signed the Treaty of Madrid.[5] But before he could leave Spain he was forced to send for two of his sons, the Dauphin and the Duke of Orleans, then await their arrival, and then hand them over to Charles as hostages. Once he set foot in his own land again, the king was obliged, according to the treaty, to send Charles a large sum of gold, literally a king's ransom, if he wished to recover his sons. The treaty contained one clause that Francis understandably had no intention of respecting. It stated that when the dauphin and little duke were restored to him, he was to send his third and youngest son to Charles to be brought up at the court of Spain.

Shortly after the two royal hostages were brought to Madrid, their father, the king, was freed, having been the emperor's prisoner for a year and a month. The galleon that returned Francis and his courtiers to France, embarked the following day for Spain with the ransom money for the two princelings.

Upon his homecoming, one of the first acts of Francis I was to designate a successor to the late Bonnivet. The new Admiral of France and Brittany, named to the office on March 25, 1526, was a nobleman of high rank, le Sieur de Brion, Philippe Chabot, Baron d'Apremont, Knight of the Order of the King.

Verrazzano no sooner learned of the appointment than he and his brother, who was resolved to make the next voyage with him, called on Jean d'Ango. Aware of his dependence on Ango's favor, Verrazzano, while burning to know the answer, casually and coolly put the question that possessed him night and day.

"Monsieur, is the plan we discussed with you some time ago still acceptable?"

"For my part, yes, and I believe Admiral Chabot will be in agreement with me. But—I also believe he will exact a condition which isn't in your plans."

"Could I ask you what it is?"

Ango nodded. "Before you set out to find a southward passage to the South Sea, and then return to Francesca to explore inland with French settlements in mind, the admiral will require you to make a commercial voyage."

"A commercial voyage," Verrazzano repeated quietly, and seemed to study his hands, folded and looking almost pale in contrast to the purple-blackness of the table top on which he rested them. For a moment or so he receded from the prospect, then acquiesced.

"Where, monsieur, will the admiral want us to go for this purpose?"

"To Brazil for wood, if possible. Then to the Moluccas for spices. You won't be likely to encounter Spanish interference in the Indian Ocean. Spanish navigators seldom use the route that Magellan opened for them. Then, too, for the time being at least we are at peace with Spain. Charles can afford to be tolerant. He is about to wed Isabella of Portugal. On this account his traders are free to barter in Brazil, Africa, and India. It is Portugal who threatens us. The danger of sailing in Portuguese waters is greater than ever now that Don John's coast guard system is in effect. His naval militia has orders not to molest Spaniards in Portuguese territory but to sink French ships and their crews. Don John's commander of the Brazilian coast guard is able and vigilant.[6] To date, Cristovão Jaques—that is his name—has sunk three of our ships, and at Bahia he captured three hundred Frenchmen and shipped them to Lisbon.[7] What has become of them? We don't know. Our questions and letters go unanswered."

It was quiet for several moments. Girolamo stared at Ango, eyes wide with horror. Giovanni sat withdrawn, considering this new development. Ango looked from the one brother to the other.

"The hazards are real," he said, "and too serious for

me not to be thoroughly frank with you. Whether you want to risk them or not is for you to say."

Even though Girolamo felt unsure and somewhat afraid, he knew his brother too well to suppose that he would back out because of danger. As for himself, he would not abandon Giovanni.

"If Giovanni is willing, I am," he said bravely.

"Well Giovanni," Ango said, "what about you? Do you want to chance it?"

"Yes, monsieur, I do."

"*C'est bon.* I shall arrange for us to meet with Admiral Chabot at his earliest convenience."

Normandy's apple trees were in tight green bud at the time the admiral received them and drew up a long and often quoted document which was written in Old French.[8] In translation, it began:

> We, Philippe Chabot, Baron d'Apremont, Knight of the Order of the King, his governor and Lieutent General of Burgundy, Admiral of France and Brittany. Having this day determined for the good, profit, and advantage of France, to give two of our galleons at present at Le Havre de Grâce, with one ship belonging to Jean Ango of Dieppe of seventy tons burden or thereabouts . . . to make the voyage for spices to the Indies. . . .

Money was needed for provisions, merchandise, artillery, ammunition, and advance pay to the crews. Apart from Chabot, Ango, and "*messire Jehan de Varesam, principal pilote,*" three other persons were named who would contribute. Giovanni da Verrazzano's pledge was for 2000 pounds, Tours currency. A great sum. Everything required *"pour faire ung tel et si long voiage"*—for such a long voyage—would be supplied, the contract read, by Ango and the admiral. Verrazzano was obliged to engage experienced pilots for the other two vessels. Letters patent would be obtained from the king in order to expedite and make official *"le voiage de messire Joan."* The admiral and Ango promised that all would be in readiness *"dedans deux moys de ce jourdhuy,"* within two months of this day. The day can only be guessed at, for the contract was not dated.

Once again Ango reminded Verrazzano that this time he would have to sail waters where he stood to lose his life. "Perhaps," he said, "you ought to give this voyage more thought. We can wait."

More thought? Verrazzano glanced up with a start. For himself there was no need to think about it a minute longer. His only misgivings were for his brother. He looked at him, and Girolamo in his own resolute way said firmly. "Your decision is my decision."

Proud of Girolamo and moved by his loyalty, Verrazzano stared down at his hands again and said nothing for a moment.

Outside, birds chirped on the budded boughs of beech trees.

"Well then, messieurs, the matter is settled," Verrazzano said finally.

Ango gazed at him as at a portrait, his attention fixed on the fine oval face, on the penetrating eyes that had fire in their brooding blackness.

"You are sure, Giovanni?"

"I am sure, monsieur."

"Do you want to sign, then?"

"Yes, monsieur." Taking a pen, Verrazzano said softly, *"C'est ma planche de salut."*

Planche de salut meant the sheet anchor. The big anchor was used only in extreme situations, as the last hope. The remark was of a kind that made one feel cold despite the April sunshine that streamed in through tall windows. Each man wanted to refute it, yet not one of the three could cover up, or laugh off, or unsay Verrazzano's comment that this was his last chance, his last hope. They turned away from it, as they would have turned away had they seen tears in Verrazzano's eyes.

PART THREE

*The Last Voyage*

# 8

ONE HOUR to midnight, and as yet nothing could be seen from the mole at Le Havre but the water, and fringes of foam, and moonlight that shimmered like a trail of pale green jewels superimposed upon the river's surface. A handful of dockers waited on the pier. They were quiet. Close by, four men stood close together. Occasionally, one or another looked round him, cautiously, as if he expected to confront a not unexpected menace. Now and again they gestured seaward, and when they spoke they whispered.

Among the four major characters in this night pantomime, Giovanni da Verrazzano was most easily recognized by his stature—he always seemed taller than he was—his lean, powerful build, and his Italian mantle with its high-standing collar and deep folds which, when lifted by the wind, rippled like waves. Girolamo hovered restlessly at his right, and at his left were the pilots he had engaged for the voyage to Brazil and the Moluccas. In the two Portuguese defectors, Estevão Dias and Santiago de Castro, nicknamed Rosado for his reddish hair and beard, Verrazzano had knowledgeable and courageous navigators. More, Dias was familiar with the ports of Brazil, Castro with the Indian Ocean.

Soon, with a rustling sound as of ships moving through a drift of dry leaves, a small fleet came into view. Coming from Honfleur to Le Havre de Grâce,[1] the vessels shattered the green moon-gems as they pushed ahead along the quivery moonlit track. Gradually the crispy rustle ceased. Dockers sprang to their posts and, without a word exchanged, caught the lines thrown to them by sailors on the decks and moored in a row the ships of Giovanni da Verrazzano's fleet: the flagship *La Flamengue*, *La Marie-de-Bon-Secours*, and a third vessel, name unknown.[2]

The crews came ashore. Usually full of talk and good-humored banter, tonight the men were quiet and serious. Each seemed on guard against an unseen danger. They clustered round their commander. Giovanni da Verrazzano, all in a voice kept low, introduced his brother, then presented the *Marie's* men to her pilot, Estevão Dias, and the men assigned to the third vessel to her pilot, Santiago de Castro. There were murmured civilities, then Verrazzano issued final instructions and ordered the crews to go straight to their lodgings and to sleep. At best their rest would be brief. The fleet was due to sail before daybreak. He was firm, he was cool —no matter what he might be feeling, Verrazzano never permitted himself to appear to be other than firm and cool—and his manner had its customary effect. It calmed the anxiety of the sailors who, having said goodnight, hurriedly walked away in groups.

The commander watched them for a moment, then turned to his companions. "Come with me," he said.

In a few minutes they were closeted together in Verrazzano's cabin on the *Flamengue's* quarterdeck. Girolamo, who was to share the cabin with his brother, drew the heavy curtains over the portholes and lit an oil lamp that swung from a ceiling beam. Yellowish light illumined Giovanni's pale but set features and the vanilla-colored faces of the two pilots. Girolamo took his place at the table with the others. They sat looking at each other for a moment, then Giovanni nodded, as if confirming an unvoiced idea. The cabin was filled with a sea smell and June warmth. Verrazzano removed the velvet beret from his head and tossed it on the chair over which he'd already flung his long traveling cloak. He cleared his throat and proceeded to consult with his pilots on a few details, then closed the discussion with a review of the daily sailing routine.

"The flagship will lead," he said. "Upon reaching the ocean we will fall into triangular formation. Until sundown. Then you, Dias, and you, Castro, will ease up alongside the *Flamengue,* report to me and receive orders for the night. The triangle then will straighten into a column."

"In case," Dias said, taking up where Verrazzano left off, "a sudden change requires the *Flamengue's* sails to be reefed, furled, or set, or the tack altered, Castro and I will follow your example. Flag signals will inform us by day; by night, changes will be ordered with torch signals. We will repeat the signs to show that we understand what is to be done."

"Good. And if a ship lags too far astern of the fleet," Verrazzano reminded them, "she is to fire one gun. Should she be in trouble, she will fire three salvos of artillery. Needless to say, cressets are to burn fore and aft throughout the night and so light the way one for the other." Verrazzano paused. A memory etched a frown on his brow. He remembered a storm in northern waters, and terrified men who despite the peril they were in were able to forget it long enough to condemn him. He sighed, as he said, "At sea, storms and mutiny can be expected."

"Yes, we know."

Verrazzano eyed the pilots a moment longer, then sat forward in his chair, arms folded on the table. "If for any reason I am forced to turn back," he said, looking now at Dias, now at Castro, "you are to go to the Moluccas without me."

Unlike his brother, Girolamo was not by habit firm and calm. He raised his head with a start, worry in his gentle eyes. Neither Dias nor Castro, however, seemed startled or afraid. Each man merely had a question, the same question, and Dias asked it.

"Monsieur commandant, if Portuguese officials in Africa or India get word of the fleet, and they doubtless will, and if they pursue and find us and ask as to the whereabouts of the third ship, what answer do we make?"

"Say that she returned."

"To Le Havre? Dieppe? Honfleur?"

"Returned, that is all. Be vague. I sincerely hope it will not come to that, but one never knows. To shun the possibility of separation because of storms or mutiny does not remove it. Anything can happen."

For some time each was quiet with his own thoughts.

None was free of care. But Giovanni da Verrazzano shouldered the heaviest load. He had three major worries: the crews, his brother, and the two defectors. Unacquainted with most of the men in the fleet, he could not but wonder whether they were as dependable as the fifty who sailed with him in 1524. It was too soon to know, and it was not his way to pre-judge. Girolamo caused him deep concern. Girolamo had changed. His bright spirit was overcast. Why? Verrazzano didn't know why, and he recalled a recent attempt to discover the reason. The conversation had gone like this:

"Girolamo, are you ill?"

"No."

"Homesick?"

"Not more so than you."

"Let's be honest about this, Girolamo. You would rather return to Italy than make this voyage, wouldn't you?"

"Yes and no."

"Look, go back to your work, go home."

"Not without you."

"I cannot go just yet."

"Then I can't either."

"Why can't you?"

"You might need me. Who knows what hazards lie ahead?"

"Nobody knows. That is why I am going to Rouen."

"For what purpose?"

"A good one. I shall have Zanobi di Rucellai draw up a will for me. I am making you my sole heir." [3]

This announcement had thrown Girolamo into misery. Giovanni recalled trying to lift his brother's mood, remembered that he had said, "I mean to give you a long wait before you come into my fortune. After I find a passage to the South Sea I am going back to Greve in Chianti. Once there, I shall never leave Tuscany again."

To no avail, his efforts to extricate Girolamo from the tangle of shadows he seemed to be caught in, to no avail then or later. Verrazzano's third worry centered on Dias and Castro. He considered them crucial to the success of the voyage. Yet eleventh-hour seizure of the defectors was not a thing to dismiss as impossible. Nothing, said Verrazzano severely to himself, nothing must happen to them. Nothing! Still and all, the danger persisted.

"So far," he said, as he emerged from silence, "every detail of our departure is safeguarded. Even so, João da Silveira's agents are always on the prowl. They can at any moment turn up anywhere. Until we are well away we are between the devil and the deep. You," he said, his gaze fixed on Dias and Castro, "stand in danger of being caught. Silveira has tried in the past to prevent me from sailing. He would do his utmost to balk this voyage if he had information about it. Whether he has or has not, I do not know. But I know that your fate as defectors would be far worse than mine. Board your vessels now. Stay out of sight. Be careful, very careful."

The pilots nodded their heads in unison, and then stood up.

"Good night," Dias said.

"Good night," echoed Verrazzano. "We'll see you in the morning."

At half-past four the next morning the crews arrived, coming as hushfootedly as when they had left the pier the previous night. Except for a few dockers, the same who had moored the fleet, the wharf was empty. At length, on each of the three vessels, sailors hauled up the anchor cable through the hawsehole in the bow. No fanfare of trumpets announced the departure of the fleet. Under foresail only, the *Flamengue* rolled into the Seine. Her companions followed. The first to reach the ocean, Verrazzano hove to until the sister ships crossed the bar.

When Verrazzano, who was more nervous than he let anybody know, saw the two vessels approaching closer and closer in the carnation glow of a summer sunrise, he had a feeling of triumph not unlike what he had felt the night of January 17, 1524. The moment the pilots were within hearing distance of him, he called out, "Set sail!"

Only two words, but they hoisted three sails on three ships, marked the start of a long voyage, and opened a new drama. Fortunately, none knew when and how it would end.

Day by day Europe dropped behind. Grain by grain, time dropped in the sandglass. Weeks of time disappeared, and miles of ocean. Having sailed 3969 miles, almost 1000 leagues, they anchored one very early morning among oriental barques in the roadstead of Pernambuco—later known as Recife—in northeastern Brazil.

Squinting against the glare, Giovanni and Girolamo

da Verrazzano glanced about them from the *Fla-mengue's* poop. "I don't see a single Portuguese caravel," said Girolamo. "Do you?"

"No, only junks and Arab dhows."

Relieved, Girolamo looked landward. The view was limited to fishing boats on the beach, reed huts roofed with thatch, and a wilderness of palm trees. "It's not what I imagined. There doesn't seem to be any life about, yet I suppose there are people in those huts. Pernambuco is hardly a village. Just a scattering of huts. Nothing more."

"You're wrong. Walls of trees and creepers hide a lot more. Dias told me. He should know."

"What more?"

"Three large warehouses and three forts."

"Giovanni?"

"What."

"Are the forts garrisoned?"

"Dias didn't say. I didn't ask. If they aren't, I am sure they can be, and on short notice. The regional government, 'captaincy' the Portuguese call it, is a stone's throw away, in Olinda."

Uneasy in his mind, Girolamo contemplated the forests of giant trees draped in trailing verdure which concealed the forts. Suddenly his attention was drawn away from the trees with their broad canopies of foliage to the sight of dark shapes emerging from the green gloom of the jungle into the hard sunlight. African slaves, tall, lean, and lithe of movement, they bounced into activity. Many pushed off in groups of threes in the jangadas, the native fishing boats.

"When are we going ashore, Giovanni?"

The other made no reply.

"Giovanni, when—?"

"I heard you." Giovanni spoke softly. "As soon as Dias comes aboard and I have a talk with him, then I will go ashore." Verrazzano gazed down at the water in order not to see his brother's look of pain and surprise which he knew would mark his expression.

"You are going alone, without me?"

Verrazzano nodded. He straightened up and faced Girolamo. "It has to be that way. I cannot leave the ship without a pilot on board," he explained.

"You aren't taking Dias or Castro either?"

"I wouldn't dare. Aside from being pilots they are Portuguese defectors. Dias has friends here, but he also has enemies. The same applies to Castro."

Girolamo frowned and broodingly thumped the deck rail with a clenched fist.

The awkward moment was broken when Verrazzano saw Dias and Castro nearing the flagship in a tender. "Good. I'll have the oarsmen wait. They can row me to shore."

"Giovanni?"

"What."

"Take an escort from the *Flamengue*. Please! Will you?"

Taller and more prepossessing than his brother, Giovanni smiled, and his sombre face lighted up affectionately. "Very well, I'll do as you wish. The steward shall go with me, and three others. Choose the three yourself. I promise to be careful." He paused, then placed his hand on Girolamo's shoulder. "*Coraggio!*"

"H'm, yes, courage. I lack it. I feel afraid, Giovanni."

"It's just a feeling. You'll best it. Believe me, no harm will come to me, so don't worry." Verrazzano turned and greeted the pilots. Girolamo called down to the rowers to stand by.

After Dias had given Verrazzano the information he wanted, Verrazzano, accompanied by four mariners from the flagship, led the way down the rope ladder and into the boat. When they landed they beached the boat. Four sailors stayed with the boat and four went with the commander. He ordered and paid for a quantity of wood, *mirim* and *brasil rosado*. Purplish mirim was wanted for ships, for it supposedly remained sound in water and was worm proof. Brasil rosado, red as *brasas*, live coals, gave a useful dye. It also gave its name to the country. Originally christened *Santa Cruz*, the vast land became and remained better known as *Brasil*.

The wood purchased, Verrazzano and the steward marketed for the fleet. They returned with a boatload of beans, rice flour, palm oil, pepper, salted meat, fresh fish, vegetables, coconuts, bananas, pineapples, and energizing sugarcane.

"How soon will the wood be delivered?" asked Girolamo, and stopped smiling suddenly when the other said:

"Within a week. Perhaps."

"A week! Perhaps! Giovanni, half a week is too long a wait in a place where every alien is suspect. There is really no need to anticipate the appearance of Cristovão Jaques in order to be done away with. They can cannonade us to the bottom of the sea from their forts."

"They can but they won't. To do that would endanger the junks and dhows. Those barques carry the riches of the East. It is more important to the Portuguese to save the cargo than to sink us." He saw Girolamo shake his head, as if troubled by something he wished he could dismiss from his thoughts. Giovanni was not forgetting his obligation to take on wood, but his brother's depression was important to him too. "Send the boat for Dias and Castro," he said calmly. "We'll talk this matter over together. Whatever they feel is the wisest thing to do, I will do."

The pilots believed there was no immediate danger in a short stay, but a long delay was sure to be considered a hostile act. The fleet could then expect to be attacked. Or worse, captured.

Off and on during the next two days native rafts edged up to the *Flamengue*. Though laden with wood, the rafts were not of a size to carry great amounts. The third day, no wood, and none on the fourth day either. The wait and the stillness made the crews fidgety. Dias and Castro manifested concern. Girolamo was morose. With effort, Giovanni maintained his aspect of composure. Whether he was right or not, he guessed that his fleet was being watched, that the officials in Olinda were fully informed of its presence in Pernambuco's waters, and that the abrupt absence of the wood-carrying rafts was a device to tauten the nerves until they snapped like overtight bow strings. His black roving eyes were constantly on the alert, and his conscience juggled with duty to orders and the deeper duty to protect his men.

Early in the afternoon of the fifth day Verrazzano was standing in his cabin at a porthole when his brother opened the door and stepped inside. "Giovanni, I must talk to you."

"Of course," he said, and was taken aback by the other's look which was odd and dark, almost threatening. "What's wrong?" he asked.

"Nothing—yet. Giovanni, you don't hold with feelings. I know that. Nevertheless, I have a strong feeling of foreboding. Please order sails set and anchors weighed. Please! Let's get out while we can."

Verrazzano neither answered nor looked at him. Sooner than betray his worry about Giorolamo's increasing proneness to fears and vague feelings, he appeared to ignore him. He stared through the porthole at sea birds that were as ashen blurs against a sky that glistened like blue enamel.

"Portuguese officials have orders to sink French ships and to sink or seize the crews," Girolamo said breathlessly, desperation in his voice. "It seems plain enough that something is wrong, that something is going on behind our backs, else the natives would not have ceased to bring wood. Can you—" He opened his mouth to say more but then closed it again.

Verrazzano gave him a swift glance and prompted him firmly. "Can I what?"

"Never mind."

"No. You have something to say. Can I what?" he repeated with emphasis.

"Very well. Can you justify the risk of staying in this port?"

The other looked at him in surprise and there was, for an instant, a pained expression in the dark, dark eyes. "Whether your sense of danger has a basis in fact or not, Girolamo, in this case it makes small difference. I had already determined to embark without further delay. Hardly more than half the wood I purchased is in the hold,[4] but human lives are in the balance. Despite my stubbornness, where my fellow man is concerned, my sense of responsibility exceeds my anxiety about wood, or any unfinished business."

"I know, I know. I didn't mean what I said. I didn't mean it that way."

"Forget it." Verrazzano reached out and cuffed Girolamo's chin with brotherly absolution. "Put your mind at ease," he urged. "I am sending word to our pilots to prepare to up-anchor after sundown."

"Thank you, Giovanni," he said, and drew a deep sigh, relieved that but a few hours remained until sundown.

When it came it was all scarlet gashes in the sky. Dusk was brief. Then, as night began to press down rapidly, Verrazzano's fleet cautiously nosed out of Pernambuco.

At the rail of the flagship's poop, Girolamo at his side, the commander watched the flames leap from the cressets. Openwork iron baskets attached to poles, the cressets held resin soaked rope. Ignited, the rope flared into red snakes of fire that hissed and squirmed against the blackness. He thrilled to the feel of the deck vibrating with the sea's rhythm, and he went back in his mind to the night of January 17, 1524. Verrazzano often reverted to that night and pondered similarities. Each time he embarked he was of necessity preoccupied with known dangers and ways to escape them; each time it was imperative to be secretive and alert. It took him a while to realize that once more he had eluded peril; once more he was on the ocean. And once again the tension and the dread of what might befall them was over and done with. For the time being, anyhow.

"I'm glad we are on our way," said Girolamo.

"So am I. But I will be gladder yet when the commercial part of this voyage is behind me and I am free to seek a passage to the sea that Balboa saw from a mountain peak in Darien. And I'll be happiest of all the moment I can shout to you, *Ecco! Il passaggio! Finalmente!*"

"Yes," said Girolamo solemnly, "the passage. At last."

Noting the change in his mood, Verrazzano looked into his face. "What is it now?" he asked.

After an interval he replied, "Are you certain there is a passage, certain that you won't be pursuing a myth?"

Verrazzano smarted under the words. "You never before expressed doubt about the existence of a passage other than Magellan's."

"I'm not sure what I think. Perhaps I don't doubt it."

"Perhaps you also doubt other things. What more do you question?

"Nothing," said Girolamo, amazed that the lie rolled off his  tongue so casually. In truth, he questioned the outcome of this whole dangerous and impossible-seeming errand.

# 9

~~~ ~~~ ~~~ THREE SHIPS rolled down the South
Atlantic to Patagonia and Magellan Strait. As they
neared the strait, what had been a steady breeze
changed into a continuous blast. Ripples deepened.
Winds veered and gathered force. Thunder crashed. At
intervals, electric fire fractured the clouds, branched
across the sky in blue-tinged sulphurous flashes, and
turned downpours into blue-and-yellow rain.

When Verrazzano's ships were more than a thousand
miles below Pernambuco, they tried to enter the strait
that forms a sinuous channel between the Atlantic and
Pacific Oceans at the bottom of South America. Aptly
dubbed *Boca da Dragão*—Dragon's Mouth—by Magellan who discovered it, the strait later received his name.
In a fierce mood now, the Dragon spewed gale after
gale. Tearing winds snatched up the vessels, pitched
them onto peaks of water as glittery with foam as the
Andean peaks with snow, then dropped them with explosive thuds. Again and again the fleet strove to press
forward only to be thrown back. Difficulties and dis-
comforts multiplied. The disposition of the crews soured.

For the most part, the *Flamengue's* company became morosely sullen.

It was obviously time to capitulate to the Dragon's unbeatable might. Hardly more than inside the mouth, they seemed not likely to go beyond it. So it was obvious too that the detour they had made was futile. To have gone from Pernambuco directly to the Cape of Good Hope and there enter the Indian Ocean would have been the shorter and surer of the two routes. Verrazzano rejected it because he would not expose his fleet to the danger of being captured by Portuguese while sailing near Portugal's African coasts, for her African coasts were said to be more heavily guarded than any others. He chose the strait instead. If they could have crossed it, the waterway would have given them access to the Pacific and eventually to the vast Indian Ocean. Unable to crawl forward without being flung back, his fleet was at an impasse. Moreover, the strength of every man in the fleet had been sapped by the Dragon's unabated violence. All were exhausted from the day and night struggle to keep the ships afloat. And it was days since a hot meal had been served, the danger in storms of setting the ships afire being too great to allow the cooks to kindle charcoal in braziers in the galleys or on an open deck.

Verrazzano worriedly pondered two needs: the need to decide upon the next move, and the need to spur the *Flamengue's* men particularly—the others seemed less rebellious—to keep their agreement to make this voyage for the good of France. In addition, Verrazzano

knew that some, possibly most, of the crew were con-
spiring against him.

He still had the rule of the ship and wanted to keep
it, through reasoning, not punishment. Regardless of
hostility, Verrazzano was not a captain to resort to
physical chastisement. He never had a man lashed or
thrown below decks and kept there in irons. None who
sailed with him ever felt the flat of his sword, or of his
hand, or the toe of his boot. As for keelhauling, he
would have withered with fiery words and a searing
flash of his eyes anybody who might have proposed that
a mutinous sailor be hauled through the water under
the ship's keel.

What was needed at the moment was to boost the
morale of the men, appeal to their patriotism and pride,
encourage them to expect success. This failing, he
would depict the danger to themselves and the ship if
they overthrew him as commander while in the Dragon's jaws and placed another in command. Not one of
them could hold the *Flamengue* together for two days
running without disaster. Girolamo qualified, but Girolamo would go down before he'd take charge if his
brother were deposed. Verrazzano knew it and the men
knew it too. Besides, there wasn't a man in the crew
who hadn't the sense to understand the peril of their
position, without an experienced navigator ordering the
moves, in this ferocious area of the ocean.

Verrazzano ordered the crew assembled, then stated
matters plainly. His sober words took effect. Heated
emotions were weighed against Verrazzano's cool-head-
edness, and the men wisely decided to let themselves be

led by this fearless navigator, this nobleman who was never found wanting in tolerance and dignity. The gravest fault they could find in him was that he was too stern of countenance and too dignified.

Soon after the sailors arrived at their resolve, Verrazzano took counsel with his brother and his officers. Then once again he spoke to the sailors. The fleet, he explained, would leave the strait and set a course for the Cape of Good Hope.

Tired though he was, Verrazzano moved with new energy as he went aft and stood behind a sailor who had been ordered to light a resin torch. The sailor translated Verrazzano's decision into a series of red patterns waved at the *Marie*. Her men saw the signals and alerted Estevão Dias. The sailing orders were repeated on the *Marie,* and then on Castro's ship to show that they were understood.

Bucking a convulsive ocean, the fleet embarked from the bottom end of South America for the Cape of Good Hope at the southernmost end of Africa. The heaving gap of Atlantic between the Magellan Strait and Africa's Cape of Good Hope might, on a map, appear to be an inch or several inches in length, depending upon the size and scale of the map. But Verrazzano was not sailing on paper. The voyage he now began was to total more than 4000 miles, a distance nearly equal to that which he covered from the "rock" to his first landfall in North Carolina.

Fair weather once more, rest, and men restored to friendliness added to Verrazzano's relief. All thoughts of trouble left him. In this harmonious atmosphere

which fostered delusions it was hard to imagine anything could go very wrong. Verrazzano didn't. On the
contrary, he assured himself that the worst was over.

Many weeks later the fleet passed the Cape of Good
Hope. The *Marie* led. Castro's ship followed in her
wake. Lagging, the *Flamengue* was the last of the three
to reach the Indian Ocean. She was not far from the
cape—probably no farther east of it than Agulhas—and
there was a cottony haze, but even through the haze
the two vessels well ahead were discernible from her
decks and crow's nest. Thankful that each had cleared
the cape without mishap, Verrazzano was not unduly
worried about his own ship's slackened pace, not at
least while he was able to see their sails imprinted
against the far pale-gray sky.

Then suddenly they were lost to sight. With incredible swiftness, scattered clouds ran together and
entombed the dim morning sun. The light changed to
olive tinged with ocher. A deep, resonant hum vibrated
on the air. Nearer and nearer it came. Stronger. Faster.
Rolling, reverberating from everywhere. Row upon row
of racing waves reared up into walls of water that col-
lapsed over the *Flamengue's* decks.

Verrazzano volleyed out orders. Men sped to make
the ship secure, but even before they could go aloft and
take in sail a cyclone swirled upon her wth a roar and a
blast. Sails split. Canvas spiraled upward and disappeared. Stays snapped like dry sticks. From ashore,
torn up bushes and fronds twisted off the crowns of
palm trees by savage gusts were borne high and hurled
out to sea. Caught in the vortex, the *Flamengue* whirled

round and round, helpless in the grappling power of the thrashing storm which was unlike any other in the experience of Verrazzano and the crew.

Finally, the cyclone spent itself. The *Flamengue* was still afloat. Not, as some had expected, a mass of wreckage strewn upon the sea's writhing surface. The olive-ocher color began to fade. The sun reappeared, full of vaporous light that gradually became candent. In the white-hot clarity, the great Indian Ocean stretched away into a distance that seemed more mirage than real.

Verrazzano grimly scanned the distance. He saw no sign of his two ships, only debris and streaks of blown foam. Dazed men gathered behind him. Saying not a word, they stared at the curdled ocean as if fascinated by its emptiness. Little by little the fact of emptiness edged into their minds. Apprehension followed and deepened, for now they knew beyond a doubt that the fleet was divided. Two ships were missing. The *Flamengue* was alone.

It was useless, he knew, yet Verrazzano sent a sailor to the masthead to con the sea for the sister vessels. Minutes passed, and no word from the lookout. Verrazzano cupped his hands to his mouth and called up to him, "Can you see them?" He received the expected reply, "No, monsieur."

"Come down," said Verrazzano, and pressing his knuckles on the rail he gazed out at the shining void with unblinking eyes.

"Giovanni," his brother was saying quietly, "what are

we to do?" Anxiety filled Girolamo. He murmured, "They are gone. Lost."

Girolamo's dark outlook tried Verrazzano's patience. He knew that the men were in shock and that their mute passivity might abruptly change into noisy mutiny. Instead of helping, Girolamo, without thinking, was making matters worse.

"They are not lost," he insisted in a voice for all to hear, and with a vehemence that blazed. "Separated from us, yes, but not lost. Dias and Castro are superior navigators. The Indian Ocean is as familiar to them as the Seine is to us. Each is provided with a detailed chart. Aided by the charts, they will reach the Moluccas, God willing."

"Yes, God willing," said Girolamo in a flat tone that implied he knew all that, but somehow it no longer meant much.

Fingering his short pointed beard, Verrazzano wondered how he could curb alarm, and then for a while at least a new hope cheered the men, when he said, "Islands linked by channels are numerous off these coasts. Our pilots could easily have been swept to an island, and it is my belief they are safe and waiting to hear from us."

His face softened now when he looked at his brother, and then he ordered the gunner to fire a signal.

Flame and a resounding boom flashed from the cannon's muzzle. The loud discharge broke up into echoes the way fire gives off showers of sparks, and like sparks that are suddenly doused, the echoes suddenly were gone.

A tense wait followed. There was no reply. Verrazzano ordered a second salvo. Another wait. Another silence. After a reasonable interval, a third shaft of glaring yellow fire sprang from the cannon and demolished the hush with an explosive rumble. As before, dead silence closed in on them.

Quickly as the tilted wave falls downward the mood of the men dropped from faint hope to dejection. Acquainted with the fear that can turn brave men into cowards and throw kindly men into passions of rage, Verrazzano summoned all his firmness for the inevitable outburst.

He hadn't long to prepare himself, for the instant the men fully comprehended the gravity of the situation they were in, they determined to force Verrazzano to take them home. On the verge of panic, they yelled their demands at the commander who stood as rigid as a figurehead on a ship's bow and seemed deaf to their shouting. In truth, he heard them with concern and sympathy, for he knew that the sea and its storms do not endow all men with courage, and those who are ever afraid of danger die not once but ten thousand times.

"Giovanni, say something, do something." Girolamo showed dismay.

"I mean to."

"What will you do?"

"I will honor their rights."

Keyed up for a bitter battle with Verrazzano, the crew fell silent when he offered no protest to their threats. Aloof and contained, his calm was as disarming as his readiness to admit their right to resist. They stared at him, mouths agape, when he said, "Twice during the voyage your lives have been imperiled by storms of exceptional violence. Apart from the fact that the fleet is now divided, this entitles you to refuse to continue the voyage to the East Indies."

Aware though he was of this right, Girolamo, torn between relief and disappointment, said to his brother, "Do you mean it?"

The other smiled at him somberly and said, "I mean it."

"Then we are turning back?"

"Yes," said Verrazzano, but he did not say back to where.

If after a while the will of the majority still expressed itself as at this moment, he would feel obliged to take them back to France. He gazed at the sullen, shaken men, a strange look in his eyes, a look neither angry nor condemning but disturbingly sad. In exchange for bowing to their rights, Verrazzano reflected, he stood to lose his right to seek a passage to the South Sea. After this dismal failure, it was not likely that Ango and the admiral would sponsor him a third time. Dedicated to a humanistic ideal, he would have to suffer it wrenched from him. Sacrificed. A dream shattered, as though it were a trifle, a prism flung to the ground, the radiant fragments scattered at his feet.

And yet, ardor for attaining his goal was not cooled by this unfortunate consequence of the storm. Clinging to a straw of hope, he told himself that in the space of days required to patch up the *Flamengue,* time would accomplish what words at this stage could not. The mutinous mood, he believed, would wear off and a nobler one develop.

"Until the ship is repaired," he announced, "we cannot go far. You understand that, don't you?"

Yes, they understood.

"Before other matters are settled, we must find a place where we can put the ship in condition."

They nodded without looking at him.

Girolamo said, "Where are we going?"

"I don't quite know. Preferably to some sheltered spot on the Atlantic side of the cape where we can stop without too great danger of being discovered by the Portuguese."

There was a flurry of activity once more, as the men went to their posts and busied themselves getting the *Flamengue* under sail. She dragged, but skilfully navigated by Verrazzano she doubled the Cape of Good Hope and anchored at a small island, apparently uninhabited, not far from the cape. The site is believed to have been the island of St. Helena.

Constantly uneasy, the men worked long hours every day and worked hurriedly, impatient to leave. Not a hammer stroke but drove a nail of fear into them, afraid as they were that in the stillness that hovered over this place the sound would spread like a mighty voice and attract unwelcome investigators. Terror of being found by the Portuguese made them extremely wary. It became habitual with them to hold their voices down when they spoke, and they were so sparing of speech that their tight-locked lips resembled scars across the lower halves of their faces.

They were afraid to talk, afraid to move beyond the ship. Water was needed and was plentiful at a pool concealed by thorn bushes, squat trees, and trees that resembled mangroves. But they fetched water no oftener than they could help. Alarmed by their footsteps, birds cried shrilly and flapped their wings with a suddenness that made the men's hearts flutter like caught birds. Reluctantly they entered the wood where tree roots overspread the ground like crawling snakes and where deadly reptiles, sometimes mistaken for roots, uncoiled at the water's rim.

The nerves of all began to show signs of strain. As edgy as the next man, Verrazzano differed from them only in that he succeeded in disciplining himself so that his outward mien presented a serenity which, not for the first time, communicated a certain confidence and courage that kept others from yielding to panic. Alone —usually at dusk and later when he vigilantly patrolled the beach—he mused on his unspoken dreads while he gazed alternately at the ocean and at the unfrequented wilderness. And when the low thunder of waves died away momentarily, he would stand still and listen for sounds he prayed he would not hear.

One evening at sunset Girolamo joined his brother. Darkly garbed, they looked like figures drawn in India ink, black against the marigold and flamingo-pink light of sundown.

"Giovanni."

"Yes."

"The *Flamengue*," said Girolamo, as though the other were not aware of it, "is now seaworthy and ready to sail."

"Yes."

"The water casks have been filled. Wood has been taken on."

"I know," said Verrazzano, who came to a standstill and looked down at the foam-bearded ripples that broke against his leather-booted ankles.

Girolamo hesitated. "When are we sailing?"

"Before midnight."

"That comes as good news. I have another question."

"What, Girolamo?"

"Where are we going?"

"That depends upon the crew."

Girolamo frowned at him and gripped his arm with a strength that showed his distress. "The men have certain rights, Giovanni, but so have you. It is your right to try persuasion."

"Yes."

"Will you?"

"Yes, I'll try to make them see it my way, but I don't expect to find it easy. When they talk, they talk only of going home, and they still complain of the long voyage they have made, to no purpose."

"Well, that's natural, isn't it? You and I also talk of going home eventually. And who can deny the length of the voyage?"

Nobody could. From Le Havre to the Cape of Good Hope they had covered more than 9000 miles of ocean.[1] Darien, if ever they reached it, would mean a voyage of about 7000 miles. And it would be almost as many if they went only to the Bahamas and northern Florida. Together with the return voyage from the New World to France, this totaled an enormous distance for a ship smaller than the *Dauphine*, sailing alone, and already beaten up by two severe storms.

Suddenly the flush in the air vanished with the sun, and with similar swiftness night came and stars quivered like jewels suspended from the sky by invisible chains. The moon gave off a bluish light. Staring at his brother, Girolamo imagined that the pearl-blue light enfolded him in a tangible mist, and made him as remote as the moon itself.

"Giovanni, you'd better get on with it. Try to win the men over."

"Yes," he replied absently, "yes, I'll discuss it with them. If they cannot agree among themselves, I will put the matter to a vote. Whichever way they decide," Verrazzano said with a slight shrug of the shoulder, "my conscience will be clear."

"And your life empty, if they vote against the voyage." Girolamo looked unhappy, as he regarded the other's sensitive, serious face, and the black eyes which, like his moods, could be as hard as onyx, then soften with the kindliness inherent in his nature. "You stand to lose this chance by behaving nobly, you know. Will a clear conscience compensate for that?"

"Frankly, no," answered Verrazzano truthfully. And before Girolamo could attempt to argue him out of allowing a vote, he sent him to summon the crew to his cabin.

For some minutes more Verrazzano tarried on the beach. Slowly he walked back and forth, back and forth, in the bluish moonlight. Head high, his shock of dark hair ruffled by the sea wind, he scanned the distance, looking westward, like a man who is not sure whether he has or has not lost something.

# 10

GRAVE but affable, Verrazzano greeted the ship's company. He seated himself and moved aside some papers on his table. Then, after meditating a moment, he addressed the officers and sailors who were grouped in front of him.

"Before coming to this island," he said, "I yielded to your demand that we turn back and not pursue the voyage to the Moluccas. Captains Dias and Castro will, I trust, successfully complete the voyage." [1]

"You trust," a fretting sailor said with a surly look at him, "but what assurance have you?"

"None."

"Does that mean," asked another disgruntled sailor, "that you also trust the captains and their men are alive and safe?" He sounded incredulous.

"Yes, it means that."

"No assurance, yet you show overconfidence."

The insolence of these two men was not lost on Verrazzano, but he was too wise to rebuke them at a time and in a situation like this.

"I am not certain of anything, though I should like

to be. God alone has the answers to our questions. What to us is unknowable is known to Him, and what to us is unforeseeable, He sees. Among ourselves one guess is as good as another. For my part, it is not in me to be hopeless."

There was silence.

Warm lamplight of melted orange illumined most of the cabin, yet the atmosphere was darkish. Verrazzano felt it and wondered what he had done or said to evoke such pessimism and, in the eyes of the two sailors, such accusing looks, when he intended only to hearten them all. His own eyes were oval flashes of burning black in his stern face. Catching his gaze focused inquiringly on them, the two sailors reddened.

"Have you more to say? You are free to speak," said Verrazzano quietly.

One of the two said, "If we make the voyage to the New World, how can we be sure we won't end up the same way?"

"What way is that?"

"I don't know, but I can imagine."

"Well, since we have no means of getting information about the men who were with us, let us try at least to imagine that all is well with them." Verrazzano did not say anything more, and noted that every man present fell to thinking of what had become of his companions. This was natural and Verrazzano indulged them in their reflections.

Actually, few if any men on the *Flamengue* were ever to discover what befell Dias and Castro and their crews. When the storm was over, each of the three ships was alone, each being out of sight of the other. Dias and Castro made for Quiloa, a plan they may have decided on while they were still near enough to signal and shout to one another. A small island of small importance to Portugal, Quiloa lay a few days' sailing distance from Mozambique, a huge territory in Portuguese East Africa. Castro once had wintered in Mozambique and was familiar with Quiloa. In Vasco da Gama's time the Portuguese built a fort on Quiloa, and in 1512 they abandoned it to reptiles, fungi, and vegetation of a wildness almost as appalling as the violence of the cloud-bursts common during the rainy season.

The autumnal rains having already begun, the two defectors chose the fort as a place to wait out the tor-rential downpours. It is not certain which one of the two arrived there first. It is, however, an accepted fact that Santiago de Castro reached the island on Novem-ber 20, 1527. Portuguese documents reveal that men in both crews later testified that they left France in June of the year 1526, and belonged to a fleet of three ships —two having been outfitted at "Ana Frol" (Honfleur)— under the command of "Myser Joam da Varamsano." This would indicate that, as of November, 1527, Verraz-zano's now divided fleet had been at sea a year and five months. At Quiloa the refugees hid themselves in the crumbling fort "until the 5th day of May, 1528, in ex-pectation of good weather."

Dreading a sudden encounter with Portuguese offi-cials, the strangers kept strictly to themselves and out of view except for the armed men who took turns serv-ing as lookouts on the two vessels. But nothing escaped the Portuguese. It was no secret to them that the men of two French ships were at Quiloa. Prompted by duty, the governor of Mozambique reported their presence to King John III and alerted Diogo Botelho de Pereira, commander of the Indian Ocean area coastguard, to seize the defectors, the crew and ships. Pereira unaccountably failed to carry out his orders.

Accompanied by forty men, Estevão Dias left Quiloa on April 5, 1528, and on May 25 anchored in Diu, a port in northwest India. The Sultan of Diu ordered them imprisoned and made conversion to Islam the primary condition for their release. A desperate letter asking aid of the governor of Portuguese India gained the captured mariners nothing but silence.

Santiago de Castro soon followed Dias out of Quiloa with those of his men who had survived fevers and snake bite. Many had died. Castro sailed too far to the south and was blown to a palm-fringed island in Sumatra. In this place of vine-hung trees and jasmine-budded verdure Castro lost his life in a skirmish with angry natives armed with spears and wearing necklaces of tigers' teeth. Several Frenchmen were slain before they could draw their knives, and one who begged mercy of the island's king was slowly roasted alive on a spit.

Terrified, those who escaped death in this murderous paradise made a swift retreat to their ship. They set sail and came to Madagascar. One of the four largest islands in the world, it was separated from East Africa by the wide Mozambique Channel. Under a blanket of smothering coastal heat they rested here for a few days,

and tried to obtain ginger, cloves, and pepper. Failing
in their effort, they embarked once more and were
wrecked on a reef in the shark-infested channel. Ten
men rowed off in the ship's tender and disappeared in
the mist that overhung the Indian Ocean like fine silver
tissue. They never emerged from the mist, but vanished
with it.

Those who remained behind became afflicted with
a kind of drugged weariness of body and spirit. Fear finally spurred them to move, even though they dragged
as if their limbs were chained. With what they salvaged
of the wreckage they managed to build a small boat.
In this badly put together craft they crossed the channel, and on July 18, 1528, beached at Sofala, an ancient
Afro-Arab port in Mozambique.

Sofala, according to tradition, is the site often referred to in the Old Testament as Ophir, supposedly
the port to which King Solomon sent his ships to load
on fragrant woods, spices, gold, silver, ivory, and diamonds. However fabled and exotic its past, to the
twelve men in the leaking boat Sofala meant little more
than a slim chance of survival. Famished, ragged, covered with sores, faces gaunt and heavily bearded, they
begged help and soon realized they hadn't a chance.
They had nothing to look forward to save the doom
decreed by John III for all Frenchmen captured in Portuguese possessions, and all non-French sailing French
vessels.

Details of the voyage from France were forced from
them and a copy of their account was sent to the king
of Portugal. Enclosed in the report was the well an-

notated marine chart which had been taken from them immediately and represented all they owned except some moth-eaten red cloth and spoiled food. The map which was to have guided Castro to the spiceries in eastern Indonesia went instead to Lisbon and enlightened King John as to the sea route Verrazzano's fleet had followed.

Only a few minutes had passed in the cabin on the *Flamengue,* but to Verrazzano it seemed an hour. He abruptly roused the men with a statement that startled them out of their wonderings.

"We are weighing anchor before midnight, which leaves us a limited time for talk. So let us concentrate on our problem." Verrazzano scrutinized them, but none returned his look. His steady gaze and the regal authority that emanated from him immobilized the men for a moment. "Our problem," he went on, "is this. Do we go back to France having achieved nothing for the people? Or do we first seek in the New World a passage to the South Sea?"

Most of the men tensed. Some showed obstinacy, others distrust. No one replied. Verrazzano was not surprised. He had experienced similar crises in the past. The pattern seldom varied. First resentment, then challenge, then a period of indecision, and lastly a plain yes or a no. His need was patience. Being a foreigner, he needed to be doubly patient and deaf to rudeness.

"You did not find the passage three years ago," a seaman reminded him.

"True. Still, is that sufficient reason to give up the search?"

"That depends. Can you, monsieur, give us proof that a passage exists?"

"I cannot. The best I can do is refer you to the works of geographers, cosmographers, and the ancient philosophers."

"Then you don't know where it is?"

Remembering the error he made in 1524 and how he looked for a headland which he believed would lead him to the "Oriental Sea," Verrazzano gave a dry little laugh. "I know where it isn't," he said, "and I have two theories as to where it is likely to be."

Another sailor asked with sarcasm, "Where is it *likely* to be?"

"Either in northern Florida or somewhere off the South Caribbean, toward Darien."

"Your theories spell trouble, monsieur. Spain owns that territory."

"We know that." Verrazzano's voice, colored with impatience, rose somewhat. Then he quickly subdued his voice and his irritation. "The risk," he said, "is scarcely greater there than in Brazil and in this vast Portuguese monopoly. The two areas I mentioned are not without danger, yet we have, I think, an even chance of avoiding trouble. Spanish galleons sail Floridian waters to and from the Gulf of Mexico. Even so, with caution and God's help we should be able to reach and search northern Florida without running into a Spanish fleet. Also, keep in mind that Florida is not colonized. The same is true of the Bahamas, Haiti—the western third of Española—Jamaica, and other islands of the Lesser Antilles. This offers us a good opportunity to enter and leave the region with relative safety."

A hush of uncertainty fell over the gathering.

Verrazzano's words cut across it. "Gentlemen, you had ample time, during our stay here, to consider the matter. For a French ship and her company this is no place to tarry comfortably. The Portuguese threat is ever-present and darkens like a storm building up to break, without one knowing when or where. We shall up-anchor tonight."

The second disgruntled sailor asked, "Are we sailing to France?"

"As yet, I cannot answer that." After a second, Verrazzano said briskly, "From here to the West Indies and Florida is a big leap and a long voyage. To each of you I say, are you willing to make the leap? Are you willing or unwilling to serve France in this venture?"

A minute or so went by. Verrazzano studied the men with that somber sternness of his that had a way of often determining a frightened man to be fearless, filling a selfish one with remorse, and shaming cowards into corners.

A young seaman took a step forward. "Monsieur," he said, "I am willing." He hesitated, rubbed his chin.

"What is it?" Verrazzano probed gently.

"I am puzzled, monsieur. Why should you, an Italian, care so much about France?"

"I am grateful to your king," said Verrazzano.

"For what, monsieur?"

"For an opportunity. Lost in 1524, I hoped I might redeem it on this voyage. Oh, it is not that alone. I care about people. And rights. A person's rights and a nation's. When mighty nations deny weaker ones their rights, I offer to do whatever I can. There isn't much I can do except try to find for France a way to the South Sea. Her own route to the Orient would promote trade and make France prosperous."

Brows knitted in a frown, Girolamo surveyed his idealistic brother with a look both worried and reproachful. All that talk about rights! Why had he not exercised his own?

There was no sound but the hoarse cry of night birds in the brush, water smiting the ship's sides, and from far off came the measured throb of sharkskin drums.

Stirred by a sudden resolution, Verrazzano's officers approached him. One spoke for all.

"Monsieur, we also are willing."

Sailors followed their example. Some. Because of those who hung back, Verrazzano suggested a vote. Time being precious, they agreed to an open vote, a showing of hands. Verrazzano named a petty officer to preside. Then he left his chair and crossed the cabin to stand beside his brother.

"You're upset," he said to him. "Don't be."

"But I am. I can't help it. Giovanni, why didn't you insist?" Girolamo struggled to hold his voice to a whisper. "You yielded to their insistence about not going to the Moluccas. In this instance you could have compelled them to sail with you to the New World."

"No." His reply was decisive and cold.

"Very well. But if the majority vote is negative, that's it."

"Yes, that's it. The enterprise is finished. Listen, Giro-lamo, no good comes of compelling men to sail against their will. Coercion breeds enmity, and discipline is defied as a punitive action. Hard feelings toward a com-mander can turn a voyage into a nightmare. I want men who freely consent to sail with me. No others."

Although his words were firm his heart was shaking and his hands, which he had clasped behind his back, were clammy. Gaze averted from the officer who was talking with the men, Verrazzano looked fixedly at his shield with the wind rose and iris lily aglow in the lamp-light. No sign of his anxiety showed in his face. Giro-lamo was different. Shifting emotions played across his features like shadows of shifting flames. And yet, un-derneath Giovanni's seeming marble iciness was a soft man. Indeed, he was an ardent one, ever ablaze with the zeal of a dreamer whose dedication to an idea and ideal whipped the blood without let up.

Sudden cheering told Verrazzano how the majority had voted. Only two sailors, the two grumblers, re-mained unconvinced.

Verrazzano's marble pose melted in a warm, brilliant smile, a smile of wild relief. In words of characteristic sincerity he thanked the men. Then, excited, his hands gestured with Italian exuberance as he told them how, after they found the passage, he would like to retrace his voyage of 1524. He wanted them to see *Francesca,* the locations he had in mind for future French colo-nies. He wanted them to see the dense forests and be-come acquainted with the Indians. He would show them acres of wilderness where crops and orchards could be cultivated. He would show them what he believed could well become a great port in the land of Angoulême. And he was eager to revisit Porto Refugio, the two kings, and their gracious people.

There was a pause.

"This time," he said, "I hope to succeed. If, however, it does not happen that way, I shall have regrets of course, but far fewer than had I not tried. Let us resolve, gentlemen, to succeed, resolve to give France a road to the East, and to take to King Francis a clearer and fuller knowledge of *Francesca* and its possibilities. Believe me, fulfillment of a goal such as this exceeds any peril."

One of the two dissenters gave him a stare and said, in a hard voice, "See to it that we get back to France. That's goal enough for me."

The angry voice still snarling in his ears, Verrazzano bade farewell to Africa shortly before midnight. Once again, as in 1524, he was setting forth with only one ship. Bearing away before the wind, the *Flamengue* alone began the long voyage up the South Atlantic, her course shaped for northern Florida.

# 11

꧁꧂꧁꧂꧁꧂ OPINIONS contradictory as day and night make it difficult to say precisely where Verrazzano was in October and November of 1527, other than that he was at sea. Things happened during these months of which he had no knowledge. Ignorant of the fate of Dias, Castro, and their men, he was unaware also that in Spain a certain man's doom was sealed. Barely known to Verrazzano except for his successful brigandage, it was, ironically, this man for whom Verrazzano was to be mistaken and defamed for centuries. The day that Charles V had predicted was not far distant had come. And when it came Charles V celebrated a triumph, Francis I suffered a loss, and John III was irate.

While cruising a Spanish coast in October, 1527, Jean Fleury and eight of his followers were seized by Spanish pirates. Pedro Botelho, commander of Portugal's European coast guard, was close enough to witness the struggle and capture. He hastened to the scene and offered King John's bribe of 10,000 golden ducats—approximately $30,000—for "João Florim," Jean Fleury, the man he had vowed to snatch away from Charles V.[1]

The Spaniards rejected the bribe. "Juan Florin" was not for sale. Such as it was, there was honor among pirates as among thieves. So off they sailed and delivered their catch to the judge at Puerto del Pico. Jubilant, the magistrate wrote to Emperor Charles and advised him that he had "executed the law" upon the prisoners.[2]

Most of the eight young men who were taken with Fleury were sons of titled gentlemen. One, an Italian, stemmed from a noble family of Turin. Especially in France and England, where piracy had become a necessity, the career attracted rugged youths of the upper middle class and the lesser nobility. Not yet had the profession acquired the odium that characterized it in later years. As to the pirates in the employ of Jean d'Ango of Dieppe, they definitely were not what the French called *rif et raf*, riffraff.

Names and backgrounds of the nine seized men, as well as the names of their six Spanish captors, were forwarded to the emperor by the judge. Relative to the Spanish pirates, the judge suggested that the six heroes deserved substantial rewards for loyalty strong enough to resist the king of Portugal's tempting offer. As to the fate of the nine, one lay dying of dagger wounds, seven were condemned to the galleys for life, and "Juan Florin," Jean Fleury, was to hang at the emperor's pleasure.

At about the same time that torrential rains deluged Quiloa where, in November 1527, Santiago de Castro sought shelter in an old fort, fallen leaves from trees turned gray strewed the cobbles with dulled bronze in Colemar de Arenas, a village near Toledo. To this place Jean Fleury was brought in irons. Here and now it was the emperor's pleasure to see the Norman pirate swing from the gallows.

There is small doubt that when Fleury died Verrazzano was at sea. Yet, either because certain historians were biased, or had neglected to check their sources or dig deeper for the truth, Verrazzano, Florentine nobleman and navigator, continued to be confused with Jean Fleury, pirate of France. For the next 350 years and more Giovanni da Verrazzano was to be hatefully referred to in some published works as "Juan Florin," even "Juan Verrazzano Florin," standing falsely accused of having been the *"corsario de francia,"* the French corsair, who was the bane of Spain's seas, robbed the ships of Hernando Cortés, and died a criminal's death by hanging.[3]

In the dark about Fleury, Verrazzano was similarly blind to the fact of a letter addressed to John III by João da Silveira. Written in Paris on the eve of Christmas, 1527, the Portuguese ambassador reported, "Mestre Terazano is going from France with five ships to a great river in Brazil. . . ."

Rich Brazil, jealously owned by Portugal, was a touchy topic with many Portuguese; with Silveira it amounted to a mania. Upon Verrazzano's arrival in France, supposedly in 1521 or 1522, Silveira informed John III that Verrazzano planned to colonize Brazil! Now he warned that Verrazzano was going to a great river in Brazil. He did not say why. But he assured his king that he had protested and had "reprehended the admiral, not without passion." An additional shred of uncertain intelligence was entered in this letter. "The said Verrazzano," Silveira wrote, "is leaving for the river in February or March." [4]

Silveira often made unreasonable charges against the Florentine navigator and invested him with motives that never occurred to him. It seems obvious that Silveira disliked him, perhaps because Verrazzano outwitted him. While Silveira sought ways to keep him from sailing, Verrazzano quietly embarked, always elusive as the far horizon rim. On this voyage one goal alone inspired him, to find a passage to the South Sea. And his ultimate destination was neither Brazil nor the Moluccas. It was northern Florida. Or the alternative, the South Caribbean road toward Darien.

After a time, a long time, the *Flamengue* reached Florida. Verrazzano knew that to dally here was asking for trouble. He made a fairly fast inspection of the area he'd had in view, then investigated an inlet of the Mexican Gulf where he could well have found himself suddenly hemmed in by Spanish galleons. Luckily, none appeared.

He pushed on to the Bahamas, an archipelago of hundreds of islands and islets. On October 12, 1492, Christopher Columbus made his first landfall on an obscure island in the Bahamas. Flying rumors spread by Carib Indians regarding a natural fountain with unnatural powers sent Juan Ponce de León from Puerto Rico in 1513 to find this illusory marvel. Reportedly, it burbled in the Biminis, a Bahamian island group. De León did not find the mythical spring, but he discovered a peninsula which he partially explored and to which he gave the name *La Florida.*

For the most part, Verrazzano's men began to consider the passage to the South Sea as much a myth as the fountain of youth. They found nothing but isles, sand banks, and reefs. Some reefs were visible, exposed. Others were hidden until seen under flowing aquamarine. Limply waving branches of black and orangy-brown seaweed covered the rock formations. Prongs of coral projected from them. If these sharp outcroppings pierced a ship's hull the wound was apt to be fatal. Verrazzano recognized the peril, remained alert beside the helmsmen, and safely brought the *Flamengue* out of the Bahamas.

Results, or rather no results, of the initial search cast a shadow over the crew. Lacking the idealism and motive that urged his brother on and on, Girolamo took a dim view of the future. Verrazzano accepted the glum attitude as normal, following upon the high expectations that had boosted their spirits throughout the long voyage. Inevitably, a touch of this gloominess rubbed off on him, but his remarkable self-discipline enabled him to hide his feelings. Nobody even guessed that for the first time he was beset by doubts. Nobody saw the least sign of discouragement. And, as always, his confidence abruptly reasserted itself and flashed like a new-kindled flame. To have come this far served only to intensify his determination to persevere. It is unlikely that at this point anyone or anything could have induced him to drop the quest. Anything, that is, except the one thing that he would not have believed possible. He had no inkling of the cost that his explorer's zeal was going to exact. If he'd known, he still might have chanced it alone, but he would not have let another share the risk. No matter how strong his compulsion to realize a dream for the good of others, Verrazzano was the last man who would have desired its fulfillment at the expense of others, particularly when life itself was the price.

Gradually, the crew and Girolamo abandoned their dark outlook for a brighter one, all patiently encouraged by Verrazzano who reasoned that it was better to begin in failure and end in success than the other way around. But was it all failure? No one aboard would have said yes. During the entire voyage it was Verrazzano's vigilance that kept difficulties from developing. That the *Flamengue* emerged intact from reef-studded waters was thanks to his quick thinking and navigational skill. After the Old Bahama Channel fell away behind them, they crossed the Windward Passage en route to Haiti.[5] A solitary French vessel of low tonnage and no impressive amount of artillery offered an easy target for Spaniards in this fifty-mile-wide ocean strait between Cuba and Haiti. High-pooped Spanish galleons sailed the passage when going to and from Santiago de Cuba, Spain's busiest port on Cuba's side of the Windward. By exercising great care, Verrazzano avoided nearness to Cuba and cleared the passage without being sighted by enemy ships.

Even so, he seems to have had a close call in this

area without knowing it. At approximately the same time that he dropped anchor for a while under the lee of an isle in Haiti, the ruthless conquistador, Pánfilo de Narváez, embarked from Santiago de Cuba. He sailed north up the Windward with six heavily fortified galleons and 500 armed men. When the flagship's prow became impaled on a reef in the Bahamas, the fleet came to a halt for twenty-five days. It was not until then that a lashing gale helped to free the ship. Finally, on April 12, 1528, Narváez arrived in Florida. Needless tarrying in Florida, the Bahamas, or the Windward could well have meant the end for the *Flamengue* and her men. Verrazzano had shown prudence and now his ship was rolling along a southern course.

His purpose was as lucid as tropical sunshine. His actual destination was cloudily inexact. It could hardly have been otherwise for he hadn't much to go on except age-old surmises, charts, and the known findings of earlier and contemporary explorers. Peter Martyr's *First Decade* contained a variety of information. Hearsay provided leads. Verrazzano's study of geography and maps, and his brother's also, make it evident that he intended to strike out toward Colombia and Venezuela. He visualized their coasts to be precisely as they were, zigzag in outline, notched with bays and inlets. It seems evident, too, that he expected to discover somewhere in this region an inlet that would take him to a river that rambled to the South Sea, the glimmery gate to the Orient.

His theory was not groundless. While Verrazzano was cruising along the eastern Atlantic seaboard of North

America in 1524, Spain's Francisco Pizarro explored to the north of Panama. He found the San Juan river—now part of the boundary between Ecuador and Colombia—and saw for himself that navigable rivers wound across Colombia's plains. It lay within the limits of reason to assume that one could go by river from some point on Colombia's Atlantic (Caribbean) coast to her Pacific (South Sea) coast, Colombia being the only South American country with shores on two oceans.

Sailing southward in search of an entry to the South Sea, Verrazzano threaded his way past islands rimmed with restless palm trees, past jungled mountains with tops that expanded into impenetrable forests. Now, too, Francisco Pizarro, the future conqueror of Peru, embarked from Panama and voyaged northward up the South Caribbean, bound for Spain. As uninformed about Pizarro's moves as about Narváez', Verrazzano again escaped an encounter with a conquistador. If he contemplated hazards of this sort he gave no outward evidence of it. But Girolamo's anxiety was plain and persistent.

The farther south they advanced the more apprehensive Girolamo became and, by contrast, the more confident his brother. Courage and intelligence were common to both men but Girolamo lacked his brother's relentless drive and patience, qualities peculiar to dream-ridden men who are haunted by the need to see a dream materialize. Despite his big-heartedness, Girolamo was not motivated by the extraordinary humanism that compelled his brother to do all in his power to succeed for the sake of others.

At times the dream was an anguish to him. Yet a

seemingly indestructible optimism compensated for the torment. No matter what, Verrazzano looked ahead to the eventual triumph. Endowed with hopefulness, he repudiated any thought of calamity. To every man on board except his brother he communicated this good feeling of assurance. Even the two sailors who had not wanted to make the voyage had let Verrazzano turn their dismalness into a sunnier focus. Girolamo alone resisted being convinced of anything save his own impression, and his impression was that the wooded islands concealed sinsister things and beings.

To Girolamo's distress, Verrazzano often went ashore. The excitement of the voyage, the newness to him of this part of the New World, its beauty, and the increasing certainty that he would find the passage soon filled him with a rapturous sense of well-being. If for a short time he managed to divert his brother, it would not be long before Girolamo would again complain of the strange melancholy exhaled by tropical nature, and the solitude. The *Flamengue's* were the only sails to blur the sky, and after a while this unnerved him.

Going back to the ship from a shore visit one afternoon, Verrazzano found his brother brooding at the table in their cabin.

"Girolamo."

He looked up. "What?"

"Tomorrow you will go ashore and I will stay on board."

"No," said Girolamo, in a stubborn manner.

"It will do you good to get off the ship for a while.

Perhaps it will cheer you up." Concern on his face, Verrazzano asked quietly, "Why are you downcast?"

"I just am." Girolamo kept his eyes on a map that lay outspread before him on the table. "I wish you wouldn't go ashore so often," he murmured, and he could feel his brother's uncomprehending gaze fastened on his lowered eyes.

"Why do you wish that? This is a beautiful land. Nature is superbly poetic here."

"Poetry," said Girolamo solemnly, "is mostly a matter of tragedy and death."

"You are frightened, Girolamo. Of what?"

"I am not sure," he said, and frowned down at the map. "I know only that it is not for myself that I am afraid."

"For me?"

Girolamo nodded.

Again and again Verrazzano said, "You needn't be. I did not come here to die. Naturally, one cannot forget that life on this earth is like the sky's azure, not meant to last. But it does no good to be always moody and afraid."

"In Italy I'm not. Here," said Girolamo, as if bewildered, "everything seems unreal and menacing."

"Your own bleakness makes it seem that way. You used to be carefree and gay. I feel to blame for the change in you, yet I cannot get at the reason for the change."

Vaguely at least Girolamo knew the reason, but he could not make himself say it. Without comment he left the chair, walked to a porthole and stood staring out at a shining patch of water streaked with sunset fire.

Verrazzano took a step forward, then refrained from going to him. He seated himself at the table, drew the map to him and scanned it, intent upon one spot marked by a small green-ocher cross. Differing in size and color, several crosses had been painted on the map. Each apparently signified a place that Verrazzano wished to explore. The green-yellow cross indicated a site that in a century's time would become Colombia's port of Barranquilla, near the mouth of the Magdalena river. In 1528 it was merely another coastal indentation, as yet unfounded and unoccupied. His face was set, almost cold in its indomitable resolve. Then all at once his features relaxed in the warmth of a smile. Mentally he pictured an arm of the rigid little cross extending and curving into a greenish river that would carry the *Flamengue* to the angular wave-peaks of the Pacific.

"Come here a moment," he called out to his brother.

Girolamo turned, and with a heavy step, as if he were tired or reluctant, went over to him. "What, Giovanni?"

"See this cross-mark?"

"I have seen it before. What about it?"

Although Girolamo's gloomy indifference stung him, Verrazzano pretended to overlook it. Cheerfully he speculated, "It is possible that we will find an entry at or near this site."

Girolamo shrugged. "It is equally possible," he said dully, "that we won't find it there. Or anywhere."

A long sigh escaped Verrazzano, and some faintly uttered wishes that did not reach the other's ears. Leaning back in the chair he toyed with a pen and idly tested the nib's sharpness. Then he laid the quill in a pen tray and looked up at Girolamo. He said, "What is the matter?"

"Nothing."

"I would appreciate a truer answer."

"All right, then. I am fearful that something is going to happen."

"What kind of something?" The question was justified but Girolamo closed up like a clam. "If I agreed to reverse course, I expect these feelings you have would vanish."

"Yes," admitted Girolamo, "but I couldn't demand that of you. Besides, trying to persuade you that what you have never seen might not be where you think it is, might indeed not be at all, is as useless as flinging a fistful of salt in the sea. Four years ago you failed to find the passage. Now you feel obliged to make amends to France. You contributed heavily toward financing the expedition, yet you insist that you owe a debt to the king, Chabot, and Ango for the right to lead it." Girolamo pulled a handkerchief from his cuff and mopped his face of perspiration. "It's strange, ironic," he went on, as if talking to himself. "People who don't know you well imagine you to be icily aloof, heartless, unmoved by the plight of your fellows. And here you are, risking everything to help a whole nation. Your determination is spurred as much by humanistic ideals as by whatever it is that makes explorers somehow undefeatable. You really care, really mean your humanism, and give the opposite impression. Even though you hide it, you're an explorer with a heart. I hope France is mindful of that and of your painfully sensitive conscience."

"That isn't important," Verrazzano said quietly.

Girolamo looked toward the open ports at the smoky-purple dusk. "I, too, have a conscience, Giovanni. Not for anything would I press you to forfeit what you believe to be the chance of your life, no matter how futile the enterprise might seem to me."

"Futile," echoed Verrazzano. "Is that how you feel about it now?"

"I don't know." Girolamo thrust his arms upward, then let them fall at his sides in a gesture of helplessness. "I am not sure right now."

Sadly reflective, Verrazzano sat with his head bowed. Moist wind came whispering through the ports. Water slapped steadily against the sides of the anchored vessel. A sailor called the watch. The bosun ordered cressets lighted fore and aft. Bemused, Verrazzano struck a spark from flint, lit a candle on the table, then stared blankly at the flamelet.

Troubled by his brother's lapse into remoteness, Girolamo made a brief, impassioned statement. "I haven't asked you to give up the search," he said. "Am I at fault because I am dubious? I'm a map-maker and navigator, not an explorer committed to an ideal. I don't have your curiosity and enthusiasm. I don't have your overwhelming urge to serve by making a discovery. But I do have a favor to ask."

Verrazzano remained inert, his eyes averted, his lips tight.

"Be careful, Giovanni. Is that too much to ask?"

"I am careful."

"Ordinarily you are. In Haiti you are more daring than careful."

"Daring in what way?"

"A reckless way."

Verrazzano's eyes narrowed inquiringly. "When am I reckless?"

"Whenever you leave the ship. You seem to forget what could happen to you and to the men who accompany you ashore."

He looked mutely at Girolamo. "You were afraid in Pernambuco too, but with reason. This western end of Haiti is empty of Spaniards, practically empty of human beings. The few Indians we've seen are exceedingly meek. They take flight at sight of us." He hesitated. "I hate to harp on it," he said, "but I say again that the perils you envision are not in the wilderness, they are in your brain. I wish you would cease to create menaces where none exist."

Agitated, Girolamo began to pace the floor. Then in a rush of rapidly spoken Italian he poured out his anxiety.

"You, Giovanni, should try to avoid believing that all is well and every shore is safe. Yes, I worried in Pernambuco. I worried everywhere. Magellan Strait was a terrifying experience. You brought us out of it. No sooner were weather, sea, and men improved than you thought the worst was over. Nothing half as bad could happen. But it did happen, at the Cape of Good Hope. Now again any notion of likely trouble strikes you as absurd, if not impossible. Why? Because we have been very lucky so far. And you are entranced, beguiled by the tropics."

"That may be, but I am not an irresponsible youth."

"I'm not implying that you are. I only beg you to remember that this is not Tuscany. It is wild, primeval country. Scary. Quiet." Girolamo's mouth remained open for a second but he did not speak. He was amazed at himself for having said this much, though not amazed that it appeared not to have mattered. How, he wondered, was he to express a fear that was not easy to put into words to a cherished brother who seemed to have gone deaf?

Verrazzano said, "Is that all?"

"No," said Girolamo, grateful for the opening. "Judging by your descriptions you could not make a swift retreat in this terrain if you had to. Ravines. Jagged rocks. Steep drops to the waterfall pools where you swim. Gnarled and spreading tree roots. Entrapping vines. How could you escape quickly?"

"Perhaps I couldn't. The need to escape is improbable. If I were ever accosted, I have my sword."

"The question is would you have time to draw your blade?"

On Verrazzano's face, lit faintly by the candle's flame, was a look of bafflement. "What are you getting at? Draw my blade? Against whom, Girolamo?"

"Caribs," he said distinctly.

Stunned, Verrazzano exclaimed, "You aren't serious!"

"Yes, Giovanni, I am."

There was silence.

They both thought of the man-eaters who found their
way to the West Indies, supposedly from Brazil, fully a
century before Christopher Columbus first sighted land
in the Bahamas. They wiped out the Arawaks, swarmed
over the Lesser Antilles, and established an outpost on
the island that Columbus christened Guadalupe. Columbus misunderstood their alleged tribal name, *Cali-
nagos,* and twisted it into *Caribales.* Hence, Caribs.
That part of the Atlantic that laves the shores of West
Indian islands and shores of South and Central America acquired the term Caribbean because Carib fleets
crossed and recrossed it constantly. Dugouts and large
pirogues—canoe-shaped boats of a size to hold sixty or
more Caribs—carried lethal cargoes of death-dealing
clubs. At night, Carib boats glided through the dark,
noiseless save for the swish of paddles slashing the water and a faint snapping sound, as when lighted charcoal is fanned to red heat. The crackle came from resin
torches fixed at the sterns, flames waving like fiery banners. The burning torch was the flag of the cannibal,
the bludgeon his ominous device.

His forehead wrinkled in uneasy thought, Verrazzano
said, "Have you seen anywhere in these waters a canoe
with Caribs in it?"

"No."

"Ah, well." Verrazzano was relieved.

"That isn't to say there aren't any, Giovanni. It's certain they have not disappeared from the West Indies.
Not so many years ago Juan Ponce de León led an expedition to exterminate them. He failed. And it is only
a dozen years since they murdered and consumed the

Spanish explorer Juan de Solís and his companions soon after they entered the estuary of the Río de la Plata and landed on the coast. Who knows how many more perished in the same savage manner! Hideously savage," he said, and then was still. Nervously fingering the medallion on his neckchain, he recalled a paragraph in Peter Martyr's account of cannibal practices as told to him by Columbus and other visitors to the New World, and reported by him with chilling directness in the first Decade *de Orbe Novo*. Remembering aloud, Girolamo said:

> They eat only men . . . If their victims are younger than fourteen years of age, they fatten them up first. If they are twenty years or older, they kill them instantly. They creep up behind them and crack their skulls open with heavy clubs. Hands, feet, arms, neck, and head are devoured first. Ten cannibals can overcome one hundred other men. . . .[6]

Verrazzano's eyes left Girolamo's face and now, as they looked at the melting wax that trickled down the candle, they were very dark and very grave. For the first time he hoped fervently that Girolamo's nightmarish fears were phantoms, not anything that could really truly be. Trying for nonchalance, he reached for a decanter and goblets, then poured wine for his brother and himself. His hand shook slightly. But his voice was steady when he said, "As certain as that Europe is behind us, an entry lies ahead of us. The search won't last much longer. Let us drink to its end."

Girolamo said, "And after that?"

"After that, back to France, then home. Florence. Greve."

As always, any thought or mention of Italy drew a cloud of nostalgia over Verrazzano. For some minutes he lost himself in thoughts of home. He wandered over the Tuscan hills, listened to the piping disputations of birds in the cool beechwoods. He entered his family's villa, a handsome squared house roofed with tile; sauntered about a spacious room with faintly gleaming furniture, carved and gilded, and a valuable collection of books. From every side of the villa, windows looked out upon terraced vineyards that dropped away to meadows; upon silvery olive trees and tapering cypresses; an islet of flowers, a lily pool; flagged walks bordered by carnations and irises, and terra cotta urns that overflowed with ivy and geraniums.

Then, in a flash, Greve-in-Chianti and the aristocratic villa vanished, as daydreams do. He returned to the moment reconciled to his brother's will.

"I'll make you a promise," he said. "No more shore leave for me, except to help the men find water. I am good at spotting freshets." The pledge given, he stood up and went over to Girolamo. He gripped his arms with the affection that was strong in his nature but which he seldom showed save toward those who were dear to him. "Don't count on meeting Caribs," he said, and shook him playfully. In a more serious vein he added, "If we hope to accomplish anything, we cannot live in fear of what *might* happen. Stop worrying now."

Girolamo brightened. "I'll try to," he said.

"Nothing," said Verrazzano with fine carelessness, "worries me."

The words were brave. Yet, in a split second something had changed in Verrazzano. His determination to succeed in what he had set out to do was intact. His poise was unaffected, and also his boundless optimism. But the tanned face seemed a shade paler than before. Most of all it showed in his eyes. Though vividly black and radiant, the look in them now was disturbingly pensive. It was as if for a mere moment they had penetrated the future.

# 12

THEY WERE standing on the poop in the full blaze of noon.

"Days pass," said Girolamo, "and it is not there. Our eyes squint against the glare, but all we see is ocean and, now that Haiti and Jamaica are behind us, an occasional glimpse of green land. How much longer," he complained wearily, "before we find a threshold to the South Sea? Will we ever?"

"Of course we will. Of course." Verrazzano spoke with his usual verve and confidence.

"I wonder where we are, exactly."

"We cannot be very far from the coast of northwestern South America," Verrazzano answered.

"Guesswork at best, Giovanni. However, I hope you are right."

Verrazzano detected discouragement in the other's voice. Staring at the sun's blinding light on the sea, he said quietly, "What's on your mind?"

"Nothing. It's vacant."

"Oh, not quite. Something bothers you."

"The heat," Girolamo said, then flung off his beret

and removed his doublet. Sword belt and sword he kept. He was never without his weapon, for he was suspicious always of Carib canoes unexpectedly surrounding the *Flamengue*. While some sent up a flight of poisoned arrows, others, he believed, would somehow reach the decks by means of ropes, then beat them all to a pulp and devour them. A cabin boy came to relieve him of the velvet garments and then withdrew.

"Feel better?"

"A little." Girolamo plucked at his shirt. It was glued to his skin. "I'm drenched. Tropical sunshine and sluggish air are doubtful delights."

"Try the cabin," Verrazzano said cheerfully.

"I did. It's an oven." Eager to divert his brother from following up his initial question with others, Girolamo changed the subject. "Remarkable! Splendidly dressed in heavy silks and you manage to look as if this sizzling weather were wintry. If you were not where you are, I'd say you were off to keep a royal appointment."

Smiling, Verrazzano glanced down at his rich but reserved attire. Silvery gray as Italy's olive trees, his unadorned silks disclaimed, rather than called attention to, his wealth. "The fact is I do have an appointment of a sort. As soon as I see land of a greenness that indicates the presence of water, I am going ashore with six sailors. They are waiting."

Instantly, Girolamo was uneasy. He stared at him in distress. Anyone would think Verrazzano had given him bad news. "Are we out of water?" he asked.

"No, but we could use more than we have. We'll fill

jars. If the water is very good, casks can be taken ashore later."

"Let me go with you, Giovanni."

The request and the note of alarm in his voice caused Verrazzano to look at him, baffled. "The times I had to force you off the ship just to get you to stretch your legs on land! Remember? And now—well why to-day in this fierce hotness that has you limp and wretched?"

Girolamo faltered. "We are responsible for each other," he said thickly, and then turned his face away from him. He did not know how to explain that for some days he had experienced a queer yet familiar sense of dread. Long ago Giovanni had insisted that these obscure fears were alien to his temperament. They were. But they beset him anyway. Instinct, intuition, foreboding, whatever its name, the feeling suggested danger. Girolamo remained silent, and his brows drew closely together.

Impulsively, Verrazzano laid his hand firmly on the other's shoulder. "You know the rule," he said. "Whenever the ship rides at anchor and one of us goes ashore the other must stay aboard." In his voice was unusual gentleness.

"Then, please, let me be the one to go."

After a pause, Verrazzano shook his head. "No," he said decisively. The finality of his reply allowed neither argument nor queries.

"Take care, Giovanni. Yes?"

"Indeed, yes. I am as impatient as you are to complete this voyage safely, to return to France with my goal realized and my promise kept. That will mean satisfaction for myself and riches for the French. After that, the two of us will go home." Although he was gazing at the glistening horizon, his eyes were in Italy. Standing at the rail of the small deck, Verrazzano seemed like a prisoner awaiting release, or an exile who dreams of home. Anticipation thrilled through him. More than ever he was certain that the end of the quest was nearly in sight.

Elated, he urged Girolamo to be forbearing a bit longer. "Who knows," he said, oddly excited, "it might happen today."

"What might?" Girolamo stifled a yawn and then said sleepily, "What are you talking about?"

"A river, an entry," Verrazzano said, smiling with sympathy. "We might find what we're looking for today."

"Oh."

Verrazzano gave him a good-natured push. "Ovenish or not, go to the cabin and sleep off your inertia. I'll rouse you if and when an island appears."

Toward mid-afternoon the wind sank. The *Flamengue* moved, but pokily as the clouds in the sky. Her flags drooped. The cross on the flag of Florence lay crumpled in the folds. Leisurely pacing the poop deck, Verrazzano stopped abruptly and gave a brisk shout, "Island to starboard!"

It was small, low-lying, and densely wooded. Growth of such thickness and verdure, he was certain, was fed by rills and springs.

"Cast anchor. Lower the boat," he ordered, and asked

that the six sailors be summoned. For a long moment he scanned the nearby island, then hurried to the cabin and awakened Girolamo. He was about to hurry out when Girolamo stayed him.

"Wait! You'd better take your buckler."

"Nonsense. I've no need of it."

"How do you know?"

"I just do."

"What if you're mistaken?"

"Look," Verrazzano said, and again rested a hand on Girolamo's shoulder, "we are close enough to see that the islet is uninhabited. No dugouts. No huts. No smoke from cooking fires. Not a soul to be seen."

"Maybe not to be seen, but there could be people in hiding," reasoned Girolamo.

"Yes, anything is possible, although I think it unlikely that those woods hold hidden terrors as well as beauty." Where another would have tried his temper in this matter, toward Girolamo he showed great patience, for he realized that his brother's love for him was deeply protective.

"Judging by the latitude we're in, do you recognize the island?"

"Only as a paradise of greenery. I expect there are many small, unnamed islands in the Lesser Antilles."

"Don't be long, Giovanni."

"Not a minute more," promised Verrazzano, "than it takes to find a stream and fill twelve jars."

On his feet now, Girolamo reached for his baldric belt and sword and put them on. He followed Verrazzano to the deck where the crew stood at the rail and chatted with the six men who awaited Verrazzano in the tender below.

Quickly he descended the rope ladder and stepped into the boat.

They pushed slowly landward over a flat, shining sea. Verrazzano glanced up at Girolamo and waved assuringly, aware that he sought some such comfort. Girolamo looked lingeringly at him. The distance decreased. The dip and rise of oars came to a stop. The boat was beached. Surrounded by sailors carrying two clay water jars each, Verrazzano led the way into the wilderness. Girolamo's eyes clung to the regal figure in pale gray silk until it was lost to sight.

Startled by the brook-searchers, birds soared flappingly out of the tree tops. Not long after, Verrazzano's voice was heard. It carried far in the silence.

"Water!" he called out.

Girolamo drew a breath of relief.

Mainly to calm his brother's anxiety, Verrazzano called out jubilantly a second time to say they had found a spring bubbling among ferns. Colder water. Clearer.

A cheer rose from the men at the rail, Girolamo in their midst. Then for a while all was still. Intent as persons at a drama who wait in suspense for the last act to begin, the men stared fixedly at the pallid beach backed by a vivid green curtain of jungle. It screened from their view a turbulent scene of water jars abruptly dropped, Verrazzano and his friends scrambling to their feet, running, stumbling over roots that tripped them, picking themselves up, panting, running once again. In a flash, the seemingly dormant island was all rushing movement and yelling.

Incredulous, their ears assailed by outcries for help, the men at the rail froze in the torrid heat.

By instinct, Girolamo's hand shot to his sword hilt. "Something's wrong. They need us. We must go to them. Move! Be quick!" Frantic, he forgot that the ship's solitary boat was on the island, the sea's depth near shore too shallow for the *Flamengue*, even if there'd been wind enough to take her there in haste, and the only swimmers capable of covering the distance were the seven not on board. With compassion, an officer who was standing at Girolamo's side reminded him of their inability to help. Girolamo's heart sank heavily, then lifted when he saw Verrazzano and the sailors burst from the wilderness and fly for the dinghy.

"Thank God!" he murmured. Immediately, his low-spoken thanks were followed by a gasp of horror. From everywhere appeared thick-set men, umber-brown. A host of nearly nude figures, each brandished a massive club.

"Caribs! Oh no, oh no! Run!" Girolamo shouted at the top of his lungs. "Run! Shove off!"

They tried to. But in a split second they were dead, killed by Carib bludgeons.[1]

Girolamo chokingly wailed and closed his eyes for a moment. When he opened them, he saw but could not believe what he saw. "It can't be! No, no, no!" With all his might, he cried out, "Giovanni!!! *Giovanni!!!*"

His cries were unavailing. No one answered him. Verrazzano had fallen forward, arms outspread, his bloodied face turned seaward. His gushing blood dyed the white sand a bright red until it was dimmed by the thin foam that washed it.

Every man at the ship's rail became as stone. Immobile. Wordless.

Wild grief and rage in his eyes, Girolamo glared at the cannibals. Now they were standing over the men they had murdered; now they were tearing off their garments.

"Oh, God!" groaned Girolamo. He seemed about to collapse. The officer caught his arm and supported him. "Come away, monsieur." Girolamo shook his head, and pressed his left hand to his mouth to keep himself from screaming. Over and over he swallowed drily. Releasing his right hand from his sword hilt, he raised it, crossed himself, and brokenly asked God to judge the seven gently. "Seven men gone. Killed. For no reason. No reason. Not even personal hatred." He paused. He was trembling. "An appointment," he went on, wanderingly. "Giovanni had an appointment with Death in a hellish paradise of greenery." Eyes brimming, he put his hands to his face and sobbed.

The wind freshened. Overhead, the crimson cross on the flag so dear to Verrazzano straightened, the arms quiveringly extended.

The officer said, "If we don't leave this place they will kill and consume us all."

Utterly blank, Girolamo seemed not to hear or see him. He heard only his own impotent shouts, saw only the premonition that had become an actuality.

"It is essential that we depart, monsieur. Try to realize, please, that as the only navigator among us you are our last hope."

"Last hope," echoed Girolamo slowly. "This voyage was my brother's last hope. '*C'est ma planche de salut,*' Giovanni once said. The search is over now, and the hope. He paid with his life for a dream. Nothing remains of it all save a nightmare too gruesome ever to be blotted from the memory."

"I know, I know." He looked at Girolamo and his heart went out to the stunned, forlorn young man. "The search for the passage no longer matters. Just take us back to France."

"I can't. Not yet. Don't you understand? I can't leave my brother on a foreign shore. Giovanni longed for home, for Italy." Still under the stress and confusion of shock, it was Girolamo who for an instant did not understand that he could neither stay with nor claim his brother.

The other was unsure what more to say or how to startle Girolamo into action. Then, glimpsing the frightened faces of the men, he tackled him with the benign sternness he had learned from Verrazzano.

"You're a man, monsieur. Act like one. In several respects you resemble our late commander. At this moment you are most unlike him. Always, his first concern was for his crew and his ship, his last for himself. Never was he deaf to what we said. Never was he so wrapped up in personal feelings that he could not banish them when another was uneasy. Your sorrow possesses you even to the exclusion of an imminent menace. Had this horrible death been yours, the commander would have been near despair. But," he emphasized, "he would also have thought of his men and the six families suddenly bereft of sons, husbands, and fathers. It was not in him to miss a chance to help and to hearten. And this, many a time when he himself needed a word of encouragement. A severe man," he admitted reflectively, "but a man with a heart for all."

There was a pause.

The officer admired Girolamo. He hadn't flinched or evinced indignation. His voice husky, he said to him, "Show yourself to be the man you are, the man your brother would expect you to be, and you will find us loyal. Handling a vessel is your profession. In our company nobody but you can navigate. And you know the way to France."

There was another pause.

A short distance away the bosun and helmsman waited for instructions. The rest of the crew had quietly gone below. Speaking to the bosun in a low voice, the officer asked him to bring the new captain a finger of brandy. In that instant Girolamo looked landward. Swiftly the officer pulled him away from the rail and forced him to stand with his back to the unspeakable cannibalism on the beach. He clutched his arms and held him fast.

"What—what are they doing? Are they—?"

"Here, drink this." The officer gave him brandy. Obediently he downed it in one gulp and returned the cup to the bosun.

"Tell me," he pleaded. "I must know! Are they—?"

The officer compressed his lips.

Girolamo groaned softly. Cold sweat broke out on his face and mingled with his tears.

"Get a hold on yourself and listen to me. Minutes are passing. Minutes here can mean disaster. Isn't one tragedy enough? Do you want the lot of us to die? You are in command. Whatever happens, you are responsible. Those brutes can let fly a rain of arrows before we can fire a gun. Come to your senses! Do something!" Deliberately sharp, his edged words cut into the shock-dulled mind of the young man who until now had displayed incessant fear of Carib treachery. The memory of it seemed suddenly to awaken in him. He brushed his hand across his eyes and gave his head a shake. "I will do my best," he said.

"Good. You can count on us to do our part. But let's get started immediately. The wind is rising. It's with us." The officer hesitated, then advised gently, "Captain, don't look back."

Brown hair stirring in the breeze, salt tears drying on his cheeks, Girolamo da Verrazzano ordered sails set, the anchor brought home, and the course reversed. Bosun, sailors, and helmsman hurried to their tasks. There was a faint clatter of pans in the galley. For even after God's nuncio, Death, has come and gone, life goes on. Men must work and men must eat. Girolamo soon had the *Flamengue* under sail. Smaller than the *Dauphine*, she equaled her sturdiness and had proved it from France to Brazil to the Magellan Strait and the Cape of Good Hope, from Africa to Florida and the West Indies. On the last lap now of a long voyage that had included four continents, two oceans, and appalling storms, she was bound for her home port in Normandy. Gallantly she rolled through a smoky fire of sundown into mauve dusk, and then into night. A strange quiet lay over the ship, the quiet that lingers after Death has fled. Not for a second could anybody on board forget that seven men were absent. Dead. Obliterated. The crew was in a cold shiver of nameless terrors.

After trouble of any kind Verrazzano had always made it a point to speak to his men. Girolamo determined to emulate him in this regard. He went out of his way to praise the mariners for their behavior. There had been no panic, no dissent, no notion of mutiny. As real as their need of him was the sorrow they felt and the sympathy they offered. Apart from words, his eyes spoke his gratitude, and in their sadness Verrazzano's own pensive ones were mirrored. Reminiscent also of the commander was the sincerity of Girolamo's thanks. Meaningfully he glanced at the officer who'd had no choice but to shame and chide him into action. A ghost of a smile came to Girolamo's lips. In much the same way that Verrazzano's assurances so often had cooled and steadied feverishly shaken men, Girolamo's simple warmth thawed their chilled spirits and diminished their qualms.

Placid while with the men, his hard self-control softened the moment he entered his cabin. He stood against the closed door and stared blankly at the emptiness about him. If Giovanni had not gone ashore, he would be sitting at the table, recording the ship's progress in the log, or checking off places already passed on the map with the crosses on it. Impossible that he was no more! Impossible!

Girolamo called out his name.

Silence.

Raising his voice, he said again, "Giovanni."

The name fell away into the stillness. Behind lowered eyelids Girolamo saw his brother. Erect and imposing, the blackness of his eyes and shock of wavy hair enhanced his tanned face. An extraordinary face. Disciplined. Tuscan in contour. Vibrant with intelligence and enthusiasm, tranquil with the reserve that was natural to him.

Why, Giovanni, why did you have to die? Why could it not have been me? You would have found the passage. I know it now, and now it doesn't matter.

Emotionally spent, he dragged himself to the table, touched the back of the chair, touched Verrazzano's pens, examined his careful entries in the logbook, and then turned away, submerged in a fresh wave of grief. Walking as if his legs were knee-deep in sand, he crossed the cabin to Giovanni's bed-alcove and sank forsakenly on the edge of the bunk. The steely glitter of the buckler caught his eye. He took it off the wall and laid it on his knees. A tremulous finger outlined the white lily of Florence, the blue wind rose, and the embossed motto: *Più Chiaro*. His eyes blurred. He leaned forward, elbows on the noble shield, his interlocked hands crushed against his brow.

How, he was saying to himself, will Jean d'Ango and Admiral Chabot receive the news of seven men mur-

dered and consumed? Of course they will express regrets, but I expect—Girolamo was to find that he was
right—that they will deplore the fruitlessness of the
venture more than the deaths of my brother and six
seamen. To one another they will probably say, What
a loss for France that Verrazzano failed again! What a
tragedy! Yes, messieurs, but the tragedy is that he was
near success when he was killed, and that his life was
so brief.[2] As to myself, who will welcome me or care
that I returned? Our compatriots in Normandy, no others. Only they and our family and friends in Italy will
mourn Giovanni. And question me.

Girolamo pictured the painful encounters. The dia-
logues, he imagined, would go something like this:

"Where is Giovanni? Why isn't he with you?"

"He will never be with me again."

"What are you saying?"

"Giovanni is dead."

"No! What happened, what happened? Was he ill of
a tropical fever?"

"Giovanni was never ill. Even in sickening heat
he remained hale and energetic, younger at forty-three
than at twenty-three. Life for him was always springtime."

"Of what did he die?"

"Courage. He died of an excess of courage."

"In a battle with natives?"

"Would to God he'd had that much of a chance!
No, he was clubbed to death."

"By whom?"

"Savages."

"Where?"

"Somewhere in the Caribbean. On the beach of a small island."

"A known one?"

"Not so far as I can tell. But I have a name for it: *Insule de' Canibali.*" [3]

"Oh, oh, oh! Cannibals. He wasn't—devoured?"

"Yes."

"And then?"

"There is no 'then.' I have told you all. Two years ago this tragic drama began on the Seine at Le Havre. It ended in the Caribbean Sea, on the Island of the Cannibals. There will be better-known and more successful explorers than Giovanni, but as a man there is no other like him and never will be again. Success was a stranger to him. Failure he knew intimately. His goal tyrannized him, not as an explorer but as a human being, for he had a heart that would not let him forget the forgotten and oppressed."

Girolamo was so inert that he might have been in a coma. He straightened, slowly. His gaze and his hands clung to the shield. With a brother's anguish he stared at the crest, not with eyes that saw into the future. Not ever had he read prophecy into the words *Più Chiaro,* Clearer, and he hadn't an oracle to reveal to him that in a sense Giovanni had fulfilled it. Yet it was Giovanni da Verrazzano who made known, made clearer, an apparently undisclosed area of the New World, an area for the most part veiled to Europeans until after his voyage of 1524. The shores and the Indians that he found along the eastern seaboard of what was to become the United States he described in rich detail in his Letter to the King. This account served later explorers for whom he opened the way, and opened to future generations a land that offered a fair field for opportunity and success.

An explorer with a heart, an Italian humanist who truly concerned himself with the needs and problems of human beings, with injustices and monopolies, and harbored the hope of independence and justice for all, Giovanni da Verrazzano never imagined that *Francesca* —renamed *Verrazana* on Girolamo's map of 1529—in time to come would receive the downtrodden of all nations. Above everything else, this is what he would have wanted, and in some measure at least this is what he achieved.

One among a host of others, the Italian historian, Roberto Almagia, pays homage to Verrazzano when he says that in spite of having been felled "in the blossom of his activity," he is and will remain "a glorious figure in the history of the discovery of America." He finds a resemblance between Verrazzano and his fellow Florentine, Amerigo Vespucci. In Almagia's view, Verrazzano's exploration of a long stretch of North America is comparable to Vespucci's navigations in South America. Combined, "their voyages give us the entire development of the Atlantic coast of the new continent from Terranova to beyond the estuary of the Río de la Plata," Terranova being Newfoundland, and the Plata an important river in southeast South America. The two

Florentines arrived at a single truth that changed geographical tenets and navigations. Vespucci realized that South America was a separate continent, not a part of Asia. Verrazzano realized that North America was a separate continent, isolated from Asia.

It is easy to underrate Verrazzano because he vanished so rapidly into obscurity and was robbed of his true identity for many centuries. But in his own way he was a victor, and his forerunner may be said to have been Vespucci, who was thirty years his senior and died a dozen years before Verrazzano's pioneering voyage of 1524. The last great Italian explorer to come to the New World, Verrazzano started later in life than Vespucci to explore and discover, and he died prematurely, just when he was in his prime and at the most promising point of his career. Weighing the one against the other, Almagia acclaims the genius of Vespucci and the magnitude of his contributions, but in conscience he concludes that Giovanni da Verrazzano "is nobler in the halo of martyrdom that sourrounds him." [4]

Whatever else Girolamo did not and could not foresee about his brother's attainments, he knew that Giovanni had earned the crown of martyrdom. Despite his bereavement, pride surged through him, and a yearning for Italy too. Still holding the shield, which now merited the crimson blazonries of a martyr, he rested his head on Giovanni's hard pillow and listened to the sounds that pervaded the lightless cabin. On the forward deck the lookout paced and occasionally called out to the bosun. The helmsman on the poop solemnly intoned the hour. Wind droned through the rigging.

Everywhere was the murmurous voice of the sea. But to Girolamo, brother and heir of Giovanni da Verrazzano, it was not seawater that he heard. It was the wind crying in the tall cypresses in Giovanni's garden at Greve.

# NOTES

See Bibliography for full titles of books and periodicals.

CHAPTER 1.

1. Guénin, E. *Ango* etc. pp. 17, 209, 210, 211.
   La Roncière, C. *Histoire de la marine* etc. v. 3, p. 251.

2. Almagia, R. *Gli Italiani* etc. pp. 333, 334.
   Giorgi de Pons, R. *I Grandi* etc. p 56.
   Margry, P. *Les Navigations* etc. p. 205.

3. Giorgi de Pons, R. *I Grandi* etc. pp. 59, 60.
   Guénin, E. *Ango* etc. p. 21.
   Hugues, L. *Di Uno Nuovo* etc. pp. 3, 4.
   Hugues, L. *Sulla Identità* etc. n. p.
   La Roncière, C. *Histoire* etc. v. 3, pp. 256, 257.
   *Raccolta Colombiana.* Pt. 3, v. 2, p. 130. 1893.

4. Ramusio, G. B. *Navigationi e Viaggi* etc. v. 3, p. 417.
   (Discorso sopra la Nuova Francia). 1556.

5. Asensio, J. T. *Decadas* etc. Dec. viii, libro ix, cap. i,
   pp. 339, 340, 341.
   La Roncière, C. *Histoire* etc. v. 3, pp. 249, 250, 251, 252.

6. Calmon, P. *Historia* etc. p. 119.
   Gosselin, E. H. *Documents* etc. p. 142.
   Guénin, E. *Ango* etc. p. 188.

218      NOTES

7. Gosselin, E. H. *Documents* etc. pp. 187, 188.
   Guénin, E. *Ango* etc. pp. 188, 189.
   Malheiro Dias, C. *Historia* etc. v. 3, pp. 66, 67.
   Peixoto, A. *Historia* etc. p. 64.
   Pimenta, A. *D. João III.* p. 112.
   Sousa, Fr. L. *Anais* etc. p. 55.
   Varnhagen, F. A. *Historia* etc. v. 1, p. 108.
   Vianna, H. *Historia* etc. pp. 110, 111.

8. Malheiro Dias, C. *Historia* etc. v. 3, p. 69.

9. *De Orbe Novo Decades.* Generally known as the "Ocean Decades of the New World." The first of the eight Decades was published in 1511, the completed work in 1530, four years after the death of Peter Martyr. Richard Eden's English translation from the original Latin appeared in 1555.

10. Asensio, J. T. (Tr.) *Decadas* etc. Libro viii, cap. ii, p. 446.
    *Opus Epistolarum.* Epist. DCCLXXI (*Raccolta di Documenti e Studi.* Pt. 3, v. 2, p. 67. 1893).

11. Bacchiani, A. *I Fratelli* etc. p. 374.
    Calogeras, J. P. *A History* etc. p. 6.
    Crouse, N. M. *In Quest* etc. p. 66.
    Fiske, J. *The Discovery* etc. p. 37.
    Gaffarel, P. *Histoire* etc. p. 20.
    Graham, G. S. *Empire* etc. p. 6.

CHAPTER 2.

1. Anthiaume, A. *Cartes* etc. v. 1, p. 315.
   La Roncière, C. *Histoire* etc. v. 3, pp. 258, 259, 260.
   Mollat, M. *Le Commerce* etc. p. 253.

2. Pimenta, A. *D. João III*, p. 113.

3. *Alguns Documentos* etc. *Torre do Tombo Cronologico*, pt. 1, maço 29, doc. 54, p. 463.
   Santarem, M. F. de. *Quadro Elementar* etc. pp. 206, 208.

CHAPTER 3.

1. Anthiaume, A. *Cartes* etc. v. 2, p. 70.
   Cellere Codex
   La Roncière, C. *Histoire* etc. v. 3, p. 260.
   Mollat, M. *Le Commerce* etc. p. 199.

2. Cellere Codex
   Giorgi de Pons, R. *I Grandi* etc. p. 57.
   Margry, P. *Les Navigations* etc. p. 209.

3. La Roncière, C. *Histoire* etc. v. 3, pp. 260, 262, 264.
   Margry, P. *Les Navigations* etc. pp. 403, 404, 405.
   Mollat, M. *Le Commerce* etc. p. 337.

4. Mollat, M. *Le Commerce* etc. p. 342.


CHAPTER 4.

1. All dates (italics added) in this chapter are those given
   by Verrazzano in the Cellere Codex. Bacchiani-Hall
   bi-lingual translation. (*American Scenic and Historical
   Preservation Society, 15th Annual Report.* 1910).

2. *Subsolano* (E. S. E.); *Zefiro* (W); *Aquilone* (N. N. E.);
   *Coro* (W.N.W); *Austro* (S). The same terms were
   used by Verrazzano to indicate sailing directions.

3. With the exception of dialogue, all words, phrases, sentences, etc. in quotation marks in this chapter are Verrazzano's, taken from his letter, the Cellere Codex.

4. Anthiaume, A. *Cartes* etc. v. 2, p. 70.
   *Archivo Storico Italiano.* Appendici Tomo ix, pp. 53-55.
   Margry, P. *Les Navigations* etc. p. 206.

5. Asensio, J. T. *Decadas* etc. Dec. viii, libro vi, cap. i,
   p. 241.
   Medina, J. T. *El Portugués* etc. p. 71.
   Navarrete, M. F. de. *Colleción* etc. v. 3, p. 153.

6. Asensio, J. T. *Decadas* etc. Dec. viii, libro vi, cap. i, pp. 250, 251.
   Gaffarel, P. *Histoire* etc. v. 1, pp. 291, 356, 401.
   Tytler, P. F. *Historical View* etc. p. 251.

7. Asensio, J. T. *Decadas* etc. Dec. vi, libro vi, cap. ix, p. 493; Dec. vi, libro viii, cap. ix, p. 641.
   Medina, J. T. *El Portugués* etc, pp. 44, 86, 119.

CHAPTER 5.

1. With the exception of dialogue, all words, phrases, sentences, and paragraphs in quotation marks in this chapter are Verrazzano's taken from his letter, the Cellere Codex.

2. Named *Carolina* in 1623. Divided into North and South Carolina in 1729.

3. Margry, P. *Les Navigations* etc. pp. 209, 210.

4. Medina, J. T. *El Portugués* etc. p. 44.

5. Asensio, J. T. *Decadas* etc. Dec. vi, libro vi, cap. ix, pp. 490, 491, 493.
   Malheiro Dias, C. *Historia* etc. v. 1, p. 239.
   Medina, J. T. *El Portugués* etc. p. 120.
   *Raccolta di Documenti e Studi* etc. pt. 3, v. 1, p. 117, 1892.
   Varnhagen, F. A. de, *Historia* etc. p. 96.

6. In his letter (Cellere Codex) Verrazzano consistently refers to the American natives by the Italian words *gente* (people) and *indigeni* (natives). He does not identify any group of natives by a tribal name. On this account I have avoided the use of Indian tribal names and have alluded to the American natives simply as Indians.

7. Here Verrazzano means the people in the ancient region of Ethiopia in northeastern Africa, south of Egypt, not

the people of the country, Ethiopia, in East Africa. He had seen many peoples from all parts of Africa and Asia during his stays in the Levant.

8. Verrazzano often dips into antiquity for a word or a name. In this instance he prefers *Sinare* to *La Cina*, China.

9. Ancient district in Asia on the southern shore of the Caspian Sea. Scythia is Tartary.

10. All dates (italics added) in this chapter are those given by Verrazzano in the Cellere Codex.

11. During the early centuries of Christianity, March 25 was termed "Day of the Incarnation." The executive branch of the Roman Catholic Church recognized March 25 as the start of the "Year of the Incarnation," and dated papal documents accordingly. A number of countries and cities adopted the custom. Florence retained it long after Rome discarded March 25 as New Year's Day. In England the tradition endured until 1752. For details see Weiser, F. X. (in Bibliography).

12. *Cimbri,* an old name for Scandinavia. Verrazzano's "promontory of the Cimbri" is believed to have been North Cape, a Norwegian cape which, except for an island northwest of it, is the northernmost part of Europe.

13. Cellere Codex.
Almagia, R. *Gli Italiani* etc. pp. 363, 364, 365.

14. The original Maggiolo Map, acquired by the Ambrosiana Library, Milan, Italy, was destroyed in an air raid on Milan, Aug. 15, 1943. Good facsimiles of the Maggiolo and Girolamo da Verrazzano Maps are in the following: Almagia, R. *Gli Italiani* etc. p. 356 (all map reproductions in this book are large and clear); Giorgi de

Pons, R. *I Grandi* etc. p. 58; Harrisse, H. *Discovery* etc. p. 217; Herval, R. *Voyage de Giovanni da Verrazzano* etc. p. 65; Lipinsky de Orlov, L. S. *Giovanni da Verrazzano* etc. pp. 18, 19; Winsor, J. *Narrative* etc. v. 4, pp. 26, 38, 442.

15. Verrazzano says in his letter that in Arcadia "we took a boy . . . to carry to France." I have not included the statement in the text because I cannot explain it and have not read anywhere a satisfactory explanation. Apart from those eight words, Verrazzano says no more about the boy. In view of his character and his attraction to young people, this is more than odd. It should be noted too that in his letter, which he wrote in Dieppe, he says "we took," he does not say "we brought" a boy to France. Christopher Columbus set the precedent when he brought West Indian natives to the court of Ferdinand and Isabella. They lived in the court and were schooled and catechized. *If* Verrazzano took a boy, he may have had something of this kind in mind, and it is certain that he would not have mistreated him. If a boy was actually taken aboard, he may not have survived the voyage, or he may have remained with the Indians at Porto Refugio (Newport, R. I.). Verrazzano's detractors pounce on the solitary statement, "we took a boy," as an opportunity to discredit him. Yet none produces substantial evidence that the boy ever saw France, or even the *Dauphine*. For lack of proof, I prefer to reserve judgment in this matter.

16. Verrazzano's arrival in New York is not marked by a date in the Cellere Codex. Through calculations, distances, and dates given by Verrazzano prior to this occasion, April 17 is assumed to have been the day Verrazzano sailed into New York Bay. In Italy and in the United States (particularly New York City), April 17 is officially designated Verrazzano Day.

17. Asensio, J. T. *Decadas* etc. Dec. v, libro vii, cap. i, p. 429.
Fiske, J. *The Discovery* etc. v. 2, p. 491.

18. Verrazzano's letter, known as the Cellere Codex (also Giovio Codex), is owned by the Pierpont Morgan Library, New York, N. Y.

19. The Verrazano-Narrows Bridge was opened November 21, 1964.

20. Early coats of arms of the kings of France show a blue field covered with a multitude of golden lilies. In the fourteenth century the number was reduced to three.

21. The "crystal and alabaster" seen by Verrazzano are thought to have been the glittery lime-rocks peculiar to this region but which are no more, having been hacked away many years ago.

22. Petra (or *pietra*) Viva is a general term for any hard rock not prone to erosion.

23. Bacchiani, A. *I Fratelli* etc. p. 390.

24. Bacchiani, A. *I Fratelli* etc. pp. 390, 391.
Giorgi de Pons, R. *I Grandi* etc. pp. 58, 59.

25. Bacchiani, A. *I Fratelli* etc. p. 390.
Margry, P. *Les Navigations* etc. p. 217.
Girolamo da Verrazzano's World Map carries this legend:

> *Verrazana, sive Nova Gallia, quale discopri 5 anni fa, Giovanni da Verrazano, Fiorentino, per ordine e commendamento del re cristianissimo di Francia.*

> Verrazana, or New Gaul, which was discovered 5 years ago by Giovanni da Verrazano, Florentine, by order and command of the Most Christian King of France.

It was usual in Italy, and elsewhere, for family members to use individualized spellings of names, specifically surnames. Girolamo used one z in his surname, other family members used two z's, in accordance with the spelling of the village of Verrazzano, near Greve in Chianti, from which village the family derived its name. (Similarly, the Tuscan hamlet of Vinci gave its name to Leonardo da Vinci). Many are the sundry spellings of the same names and words as given by Verrazzano in the Cellere Codex, by Maggiolo on his Map (1527) and by Girolamo da Verrazzano on his World Map of 1529, now in the Vatican Library. In the above order given, are a few examples: "Armellini," "Armelines," "Armilline"; "Aloysia," "Luisa," "Loisa"; "Angoulême," "Anguilema," "Angolemme"; "La Tre Figlie di Navarra," "Le Figole de Navarrin," "Le Figle di Navarre"; "Terra di Mala Gente," "Terra de Multa Gente," "Terra ond' è Mala Gente."

26. Bacchiani, A. *I Fratelli* etc. p. 381.

CHAPTER 6.

1. The name of Verrazzano's amanuensis is not known. There is little doubt that he was a Norman. Some scholars suggest that he might have been Pierre Crignon or one of the two Parmentier brothers, Jean and Raoul. All were friends of Verrazzano and belonged to Jean d'Ango's inner circle of intellectuals, and each of the three was a writer of local renown.

2. Until the Cellere Codex was found in 1909 (the first notice of it appeared in the *Giornale d'Italia*, Oct. 7, 1909), the only documentary witnesses to Verrazzano's voyage of 1524 were two Italian copies (more or less copies) of the letter dispatched to Tedaldi and/or Sartini. These were popularly tagged "Ramusio" and

"Carli." Ramusio (see Bibliography) edited and incorporated the letter in the 3rd volume of his *Navigationi* etc., 1556. In 1582 England's Richard Hakluyt translated and printed the Ramusio letter in his *Divers Voyages*.

The letter addressed to Bernardo Carli by Verrazzano found its way to the library of the Strozzi Palace in Florence and later was acquired by the Biblioteca Nazionale di Firenze. It is Codex Magliabecchiana xiii, 89, c4.

Joseph Cogswell translated this letter from the Italian into English in 1841. The letter was printed in Rome in 1844, with an article on Verrazzano by George W. Greene, the American Consul in Rome. Greene mistakenly referred to "Fernando" Carli instead of Bernardo. The error is still repeated.

Of the three letters, Cellere, Ramusio, and Carli, the Cellere stands alone. Aside from the marginal annotations in Verrazzano's own handwriting, it has value and interest in its richness of detail. The text shows a lover of nature, of scientific knowledge and curiosity; a man of humanistic culture. The vitality that marks the Cellere is not mirrored in the Ramusio version, due perhaps to the fact that Ramusio was a travel writer who gave in to the not uncommon temptation of one writer trying to improve upon the work of another. On the whole, however, the Ramusio letter is closer to the Cellere than to the Carli. While not without interest, the Carli version gives the impression that Verrazzano was tired of repeating the details of the voyage when he dictated this letter, and omitted more than he would otherwise have included.

3. July 8, 1524, is the last date given by Verrazzano in the Cellere Codex.

4. The last will and testament of Giovanni da Verrazzano.

CHAPTER 7.

1. Murphy, H. C. *The Voyage of Verrazzano*. p. 145. This book, published in 1875, makes it obvious that the author was familiar with numerous works which gave the facts about Verrazzano and his voyage of 1524. Authors prior to 1875 who identify Verrazzano as Verrazzano, not "Florin," form a considerable list: Ramusio (1556); Belleforest (1570); Hakluyt (1582); Tiraboschi (1805); Estancelin (1832); Tytler (1832); Cogswell (1844); Guérin (1847, 1851, 1852); Brodhead (1853); Freville de Lorme (1857); Kohl (1862, 1869); Correa (1862); Margry (1867).

Murphy's translations of parts of the works of some of the above mentioned show him to have been a linguist and a scholar, a fact which makes his insistence that Verrazzano was the "French pirate Juan Florin" all the more difficult to understand. He seems to have relied mainly on Peter Martyr, who never knew Verrazzano, and on the Spanish historians, Herrera and Barcia. Murphy's influence made itself felt on George Bancroft, who deleted all mention of Verrazzano in his revised (1876) edition of the *History of the United States*. Unhappily, Mr. Murphy perpetuated, without reservations, an error which amounts to a grave injustice.

2. *Archivo Storico Italiano*. Appendici Tomo ix, pp. 53-55. Firenze, 1853.
Bacchiani, A. *I Fratelli* etc. p. 381.
N. Y. State Local History Source Leaflets (*Verrazzano's Voyage* etc), 1916
*Raccolta di Documenti* etc. pt. 3, v. 2, pp. 343-344. 1893.

3. Bradford, W. *Correspondence* etc. pt. 1, p. 109.
Santarem, M. F. *Quadro Elementar* etc. p. 208.

4. Bradford, W. *Correspondence* etc. pt. 1, pp. 220, 221.

5. Bradford, W. *Correspondence* etc. pt. 1, p. 199.
   Santarem, M. F. *Quadro Elementar* etc. p. 217.

6. Calogeras, J. P. *A History* etc. p. 3, 6.

7. Beauchamp, A. de. *Histoire* etc. v. 1, pp. 52, 53.
   Calmon, P. *Historia* etc. v. 1, pp. 115, 116.
   Malheiro Dias, C. *Historia* etc. v. 3, pp. 59, 60, 70, 71, 73.
   Peixoto, A. *Historia* etc. pp. 62, 64.
   Pomba, R. *Historia* etc. p. 55.
   Savon, M. *Descubrimientos* etc. p. 34.
   Varnhagen, F. A. *Historia* etc. v. 1, pp. 108, 109, 112, 113.
   Vianna, H. *Historia* etc. v. 1, pp. 54, 56.

8. Bacchiani, A. *I Fratelli* etc. pp. 374, 382, 385.
   Freville de Lorme, E. de. *Mémoire* etc. v. 2, pp. 432, 433, 434.
   Guénin, E. *Ango* etc. pp. 75, 76, 78, 79.
   Margry, P. *Les Navigations* etc. pp. 194, 195, 196.
   Mollat, M. *Le Commerce* etc. pp. 417-418.
   *Raccolta di Documenti* etc. pt. 5, v. 2, p. 247. 1894.

CHAPTER 8.

1. The identity of the port from which Verrazzano embarked with three ships is questioned. The ports most often named are Dieppe, Fécamp, and Le Havre. The majority opinion is Le Havre. Founded by Francis I in 1521, Le Havre was Normandy's newest port.

2. According to mariners on the *Marie* and the ship whose name is not given, who were queried by Portuguese authorities in India and in Mozambique, the fleet of three ships left France in "June, 1526," (Lobato, A. *A Expanção* etc. v. 2, p. 80). Correa (*Lendas* etc. v. 3, p. 239) claims that in 1527 there left from France "three armed ships." Toward the end of 1527, the Portuguese ambassador in Paris wrote to Don John III that *"mestre*

*Terezano"* was leaving for Brazil with "five ships" in "February or March," of 1528. Apart from the ambassador's letter, no other Portuguese document has been found which says anything about Verrazzano being in Brazil, Portuguese Africa, or in Portuguese India in 1528, with five ships. Lobato, Brandão, and Correa tell us that "three ships" were armed and outfitted in "Anafrol" (Honfleur) by *"myser joam de Varamsano."* Details of the voyage, as well as charts, were sent to Lisbon so that Don John III could see which route Verrazzano had taken. (Lobato, *A Expanção* etc. v. 2, p. 80).

Sources which account for only three ships are the following:
Anthiaume, A. *Cartes* etc. v. 2, pp. 401, 420, 440.
Brandão, M. *O Proceso* etc. pp. 298, 299.
Calmon, P. *Historia* etc. v. 1, p. 115.
Correa, G. *Lendas* etc. v. 3, p 239.
Lobato, *A Expanção* etc. v. 2, pp. 76, 77.
Malheiro Dias, C. *Historia* etc. v. 3, p. 73.
Margry, P. *Les Navigations* etc. pp. 192, 193.
Navarrete, M. F. *Colleción* etc. v. 5, pp. 231, 232.
Varnhagen, F. A. *Historia* etc. v 1, pp. 110, 111.

3. Guénin, E. *Ango* etc. pp. 77, 78.
Gosselin, E. H. *Documents* etc. pp. 157, 158.
La Roncière, C. *Histoire* etc. v. 3, pp. 265, 266, 268, 269.
*Raccolta di Documenti* etc. pt. 5, v. 2, p. 248. 1894.

4. Anthiaume, A. *Cartes* etc. v. 2, p. 74.
Emmanuele, M. *La France* etc. p. 50.

CHAPTER 9.

1. Approximate mileage of the voyage: from Le Havre to Pernambuco (Recife) 3969 miles; from Pernambuco to Magellan Strait 1372 miles; from Magellan Strait to the Cape of Good Hope 4132 miles.

Chapter 10.

1. For a detailed account of the fate of Estevão Dias, Santiago de Castro, and the seamen on their vessels, see the following:
Brandão, M. *O Proceso* etc. pp. 298, 299.
Correa, G. *Lendas* etc. v. 3, pp. 238, 239, 240, 241.
La Roncière, C. *Histoire* etc. v. 3, pp. 268, 269, 279, 280.
Lobato, A. *A Expanção* etc. v. 2, pp. 71, 75, 76, 77, 78, 79, 80, 81.
Sousa Viterbo, F. *Trabalhos* etc. v. 1, pp. 83, 84, 85.
Torre do Tombo. *Papeis da Casa de S. Lourenço.* v. i, f. 407.

Chapter 11.

1. Guénin, E. *Ango* etc. p. 245.
La Roncière, C. *Histoire* etc. v. 3, p. 254.

2. Guénin, E. *Ango* etc. pp. 243, 244, 245, 246, 247, 248.
*Raccolta di Documenti* etc. pt. 5, v. 2, pp. 245, 246. 1894.

3. Barcia, A. de. *Ensayo* etc. (*Raccolta di Documenti* etc. pt. 5, v. 2, p. 251. 1894).

4. *Alguns Documentos* etc. T. T. cc., pt. 1, maço 38, doc. 57, p. 490.
Guénin, E. *Ango* etc. pp. 80, 81.
Hugues, L. *Il Navigatore* etc. p. 7.
Malheiro Dias, C. *Historia* etc. v. 2, p. 383.
Santarem, M. F. *Quadro Elementar* etc. p. 239.

5. Almagia, R. *Gli Italiani* etc. pp. 370, 371.
Bacchiani A. *I Fratelli* etc. pp. 382, 386, 387.

6. Eden, R. (Tr. Arber, E.). *The First Three Books* etc. pp. 229, 230.
*Raccolta di Documenti* etc. pt. 3, v. 1, p. 128. 1892.
Southey, R. *History* etc. p. 25.

CHAPTER 12.

1. Almagia, R. *Gli Italiani* etc. pp. 370, 371.
   Bacchiani, A. *I Fratelli* etc. pp. 387, 396, 397, 398.

2. The year 1485 is generally accepted as the year of Giovanni da Verrazzano's birth.

3. The precise spot in the Caribbean where Verrazzano and his six companions were slaughtered is not known. Surmises include the Bahamas, the vicinity of the Windward Passage, Guadalupe, Mariagalante, Venezuela, and the coastline between Venezuela and Colombia. If nothing else, one can accept Almagia's statement that Verrazzano and his six sailors were killed "in some solitary island of the Caribbean Sea." After his return to Italy, Girolamo da Verrazzano told Paolo and Giulio Giovio that they had sailed to Florida, then to the Bahamas ("Cabaco et Bahama"—probably Abaco and Great Bahama); from there, they set a southward course toward Darien (see Bacchiani, A. *I Fratelli* etc. pp. 396, 397, 398). A generic term, Darien, the former name of Panama, encompassed the entire northern coast of South America, from the Isthmus of Panama to the mouth of the Orinoco River, in Venezuela.

   If the island had had a name, Girolamo da Verrazzano, a cartographer of considerable experience and knowledge, would have given the name. When he made his World Map in Rome, in 1529, he placed the island on his map and named it *Insule de' Canibali,* Island of the Cannibals. It was also in Rome that he gave his eyewitness report of Giovanni's death to family friends, Cardinal Giovio and his nephew Bishop Giulio Giovio. The latter put the account into his Latin prose-poem, a work which gives biographical sketches of navigators, explorers, and conquerors of the sixteenth century. As poetry, his *History* has no value; as capsuled history it has interest. The bit about Giovanni da Verrazzano does not spare the reader the gory details. Professor Bacchiani translated Giovio's so called poem from Latin into Italian. The part concerning Verrazzano in the Giovio-Bacchiani *Historia* is included in Bacchiani's *I Fratelli* etc. René Herval made a French translation of the same account.

4. Almagia, R. *Gli Italiani* etc. pp. 373, 374.

# BIBLIOGRAPHY

Abreu, João Capistrano de, *Capitulas de Historia Colonial* (*1500-1800*). Rio de Janeiros, M. Orosco & Co. 1907.

*Alguns Documentos do Archivo Nacional da Torre do Tombo*, Lisboa, Impr. Nacional. 1892.

Almagia, Roberto, *Gli Italiani Primi Esploratori Dell' America*. Roma, La Libreria dello Stato. 1937.

*American Scenic and Historical Preservation Society*, Annual Report. Vol. 15, 1910.

Anghiera, Pedro Martir de, *Décadas del Nuevo Mundo* (vertidas del Latin . . . por el Dr. Don Joaquín Torres Asensio). Buenos Aires, Bajel. 1944.

Anthiaume, L'Abbé Albert, *Cartes Marines Constructions Navales Voyages de Découvertes ches les Normands 1500-1650*. 2 vols. Paris, Dumont. 1916.

*Archivo Storico Italiano*, Appendici tomo ix. Firenze, 1852.

Asensio, Joaquín Torres, *Décadas del Nuevo Mundo*. (Library files also list the translator's name under Torres). Buenos Aires, Bajel. 1944.

Asseline, David, *Les Antiquitez et Chroniques de la ville de Dieppe*. 2 vols. Dieppe, Emile Delevoye. 1874.

Avezac, Armand, *Considerations Géographiques sur l'Histoire du Brésil*. Paris, Martinet. 1857.

Bacchiani, Alessandro, *I Fratelli da Verrazzano e l'eccidio di una spedizione italo-francese in America.* (Bollettino della Reale Società Geografica Italiana. Ser. vi, vol. ii, Luglio-Settembre 1925. pp. 373-400. Roma).

Bacchiani, Alessandro, *Il Commentario della "Delfina" e del suo viaggio.* (*American Scenic and Historical Preservation Society,* Annual Report v. 15, 1910).

Barcia Carballido y Zuñiga, Andrés Gonzales de, *Ensayo cronológico para la Historia General de la Florida,* etc. Madrid, Nicolas R. Franco. 1723.

Beauchamp, Alphonse de, *Histoire du Brésil.* vol. 1. Paris, Eymery. 1815.

Beaurepaire, Charles de, *Chronique Normande de Pierre Cochon.* Rouen, Brument. 1870.

Belleforest, François de, *L'Histoire Universelle du Monde* etc. Paris, Chez Mallot. 1570.

Berchet, Guglielmo, *Raccolta da G. Berchet (Raccolta di Documenti e Studi.* pt. 3, vol. 2. Rome. 1893).

Berchet, Guglielmo, *Raccolta di mappamondi e carte nautiche del XIII al XVI secolo.* Venezia, F. Ongania. 1871-1881.

Bicknell, Thomas W., *The History of the State of Rhode Island.* 3 vols. New York, The American Historical Society, Inc. 1920.

Bradford, William, *Correspondence of the Emperor Charles V.* Pt. I. London, Richard Bentley. 1850.

Brandão, Mario, (Ed.) *O Proceso na Inquisição de mestre João da Costa.* Coimbra, Universidade de Coimbra. 1944.

Bréard, Charles, *Les Archives de la ville de Honfleur.* Paris, Picard. 1885.

Bréard, Charles, *Le Vieux Honfleur et ses marins,* etc. Rouen, Cagniard. 1897.

Bréard, Charles, et Philippe Barrey, *Documents relatifs a la marine Normande au XV et XVI siècles.* Rouen, Cagniard. 1906.

Bréard, Charles et Paul Bréard, *Documents relatifs a la marine Normande.* Rouen, Cagniard. 1906.

Brebner, John, *The Explorers of North America. 1492-1806.* London, A. and C. Black. 1964.

Brevoort, J. C., *Verrazano The Navigator.* New York, Argus Co. 1874.

Brodhead, John R., *History of the State of New York.* New York, Harper & Bros. 1853.

Burpee, Lawrence, *The Search for the Western Ocean.* vol. 1. New York, Macmillan Co. 1936.

Calmon, Pedro, *Historia do Brasil.* vol. 1. (1500-1600). Brasiliana. Ser. 5, v. 176. São Paulo, Companhia Editora Nacional. 1939.

Calogeras, João P., *A History of Brazil.* (Tr. Percy A. Martin). New York, Russell & Russell. 1963.

Carroll, Charles, *Rhode Island: three centuries of democracy.* New York, Lewis Historical Publishing Co. Inc. 1932.

*Catalogue des actes de François I.* Vol. 1, no. 2305. Paris, M. Picot. 1888.

Cellere Codex, Bi-lingual translation in *American Scenic and Historical Preservation Society.* Annual Report. Vol. 15, 1910. Bacchiani Italian translation in *Bollettino della Società Geografica Italiana.* Fasc. XI, pp. 1274-1323. Rome, 1909.

Cogswell, Joseph G., *The Voyages of John de Verrazzano Along the Coast of North America from Carolina to Newfoundland.* (New York Historical Society, Ser. 2, vol. 1. 1841).

*Collections of New York Historical Society.* 1809.

Correa, Gaspar, *Lendas da India*. Vol. 3. Lisboa, Academia Real de Sciencias. 1862. (Library files also list the author's name under Correia).

Covington, Harry F., *The Discovery of Maryland or Verrazzano's Visit to the Eastern Shore*. (Maryland Historical Magazine. Vol. X, no. 3. September 1915).

Crouse, Nellis M., *In Quest of the Western Ocean*. New York, William Morrow & Co. 1928.

De Costa, Benjamin F., *Verrazzano: a motion for the stay of judgment*. New York, 1876.

De Costa, Benjamin F., *Verrazzano The Explorer*. New York, A. S. Barnes & Co. 1881.

Eden, Richard, *The First Three English Books on America. 1511-1555*. (Tr. and ed. Edward Arber). Birmingham, 1885.

*Elogio de Giovanni da Verrazzano fiorentino scopritore della nuova Francia nel secolo XVI*. Firenze, Allegrini e Comp. 1769.

Emmanuele, Marthe, *La France et l'exploration Polaire*. Paris, Nouvelle Editions Latines. 1959.

Estancelin, Louis, *Recherches sur les voyages et découvertes des navigateurs Normands en Afrique, dans les Indes Orientales, et en Amérique*. Paris, A. Pinard. 1832.

Fiske, John, *The Discovery and Colonization of North America*. Boston, Ginn & Co. 1905.

Freville de Lorme, Ernest de, *Mémoire sur le commerce Maritime de Rouen*. 2 vols. Rouen, A. Péron. 1857.

Gaffarel, Paul, *Histoire du Brésil Français au seizieme siècle*. Paris, Maisonneuve. 1878.

Giorgi de Pons, R., *I Grandi Navigatori Italiani*. Firenze, Alfani e Venturi. 1929.

Giovio, Paolo, *Elogia Virorum*. Basileae, Petri Pernae. 1575.

Giovio, Paolo, *Gli Elogi*. Tr. M. Domenichi Vinegia. Appresso Francesco Lorenzini da Turino. 1559.

Gosselin, Edouard Hippolyte, *Documents authentiques et inédits pour servir a l'histoire de la marine Normande et du commerce Rouennais pendant les XVI et XVII siècles*. Rouen, H. Boissel. 1876.

Graham, Gerold S., *Empire of the North Atlantic*. Toronto, University of Toronto Press. 1950.

Gravière, Jurien de la, *Les Marins du XV et du XVI siècle*. 2 vols. Paris, E. Plon. 1879.

Gravier, Gabriel, *Les Normands sur la Route des Indes*. Rouen, E. Cagniard. 1880.

Gravier, Gabriel, *Les Voyages de Giovanni de Verrazano sur les côtes d'America*, etc. Rouen, E. Cagniard. 1898.

Greene, George W., *A Short History of Rhode Island*. Providence, J. A. and R. A. Reid. 1877.

Guénin, Eugène, *Ango et ses pilotes d'après des documents inédits, tirés des archives de France, de Portugal, et de'Espagne*. Paris, Impr. Nationale. 1901.

Guérin, Léon, *Histoire Maritime de France*. Paris, Dufour et Mulat. 1851-1852.

Guérin, Léon, *Les Navigateurs français; histoire des navigations* etc. Paris, Belin-Leprieur et Morizot. 1847.

Hakluyt, Richard, *Divers Voyages* etc. London, Dawson, Woodcocke. 1582.

Hakluyt, Richard, *The Principal Navigations, Voyages* etc. (3 books in 1). London, G. Bishop. 1598.

Hall, Edgar H., *Giovanni da Verrazzano's Report to Francis I. July 8, 1524. The History of the Dauphine and its voyages*. (Cellere Codex. English translation with introduction by E. H. Hall. *American Scenic and Historical Preservation Society*, Annual Report, vol. 15, pp. 135-226. 1910).

Harrisse, Henry, *Nouvelle Recherches sur l'histoire de l'Amérique*. Paris, Gouverneur. 1890.

Harrisse, Henry, *The Discovery of North America*. London, Henry Stevens & Son. 1892; Paris, H. Welter. 1892.

Herval, René, *Giovanni da Verrazzano et les Dieppois a la recherche du Cathay (1524-1528)*. Caen, Jouan & Bigot. 1933.

Herval, René, *Voyage de Giovanni da Verrazzano a la Francesca*. (*Colonies et empires*. Ser. 2, parts 1-5. Paris, Presses Universitaires de France. 1946).

Hugues, Luigi, *Chronologia delle scorperta e delle e esplorazioni geografiche dall' anno 1492 a tutto il secolo XIX*. Milano, Hoepli. 1903.

Hugues, Luigi, *Di Un Nuovo Documento Attinente a Giovanni da Verrazzano*. Casale di Monferrato, C. Cassone. 1895.

Hugues, Luigi, *Giovanni da Verrazzano*. (*Raccolta di Documenti e Studi*. pt. 5, vol. 2, pp. 221-251. Rome. 1894).

Hugues, Luigi, *Il Navigatore Italiano Giovanni da Verrazzano e il corsaro Francese Giovanni Florin*. Casale di Monferrato, Tarditi. 1900.

Hugues, Luigi, *Sulla Identità del Fiorentino Giovanni da Verrazzano con Giovanni Florin*. Casale di Monferrato, Cassone. 1897.

*John III, Letters of John III. 1521-1557*. (Portuguese text translated and edited by J. F. M. Ford). Cambridge, Harvard University Press. 1931.

Julien, Charles A., *Les Voyages de Découverte et les Premiers Etablissements (XV-XVI) siècles*. (*Colonies et empires*. Ser. 3, vol. 1. Paris, Presses Universitaires de France. 1948).

Kohl, Johann Georg, *A Descriptive Catalogue of those Maps, Charts, and Surveys relating to America* etc. Washington, H. Polkinkorn. 1857.

Kohl, Johann Georg, *A History of the Discovery of the East Coast of North America*. (In *Documentary History of the State of Maine*). Tr. and ed. William Willis. Portland, Bailey & Noyes. 1869.

Kohl, Johann Georg, *A Popular History of the Discovery of America.* 2 vols. Tr. Major R. R. Noel. London, Chapman and Hall. 1862.

La Roncière, Charles de, *Histoire de la découverte de la terre; explorateurs et conquerants.* Paris, Larousse. 1938.

La Roncière, Charles de, *Histoire de la marine Française.* vol. 3. Paris, E. Plon. 1934. (Revised edition).

La Roncière, Charles de, *What the French Have Done in America From the Discovery to the Opening of the Isthmus of Panama.* Paris, Plon-Nourrit et Cie. 1915.

*Les Explorateurs Célèbres.* Genève et Paris, Lucien Mazenod, 1947.

Lipinsky de Orlov, Lino S., *Giovanni da Verrazzano, the Discoverer of New York Bay.* New York, 1957.

Lippincott, Bertram, *Indians, Pioneers, and High Society: a Rhode Island Sampler.* Philadelphia, Lippincott. 1961.

Lobato, Alexandre, *A Expanção Portuguesa em Moçambique de 1498-1530.* vol. 2. Lisboa, Agência Geral do Ultramar Divisão Publicaçoẽs e Biblioteca. 1954-1960.

Malheiro Dias, Carlos, *Historia de Colonização Portuguesa do Brasil.* 3 vols. Porto, Litografia Nacional. 1921-1924.

Margry, Pierre, *Les Navigations Françaises et la Révolution maritime du XIV au XVI siècle d'après les documents inèdits tirés de France, d'Angleterre, d'Espagne, et d'Italie.* Paris, Jouast. 1867.

Matos, Luis de, *Les Portugais en France au XVI siècle.* Coimbra, R. Fernandes Tomas. 1952.

Medina, José T., *El Portugués Estéban Gómez.* Santiago de Chile, Elzeviriana. 1908.

Mollat, Michel, *Le Commerce Maritime Normand a la Fin Du Moyen Age.* Paris, Les Petits-Fils de Plon et Nourrit. 1952.

Murphy, Henry C., *The Voyage of Verrazzano*. Albany, Munsell. 1875.

Navarrete, Martín Francisco de, *Colección de Los Viajes y Descubrimientos* etc. Vol. 5. Madrid, Impr. Nacional. 1837.

Newton, Arthur P. (ed.), *The Great Age of Discovery*. London, University of London Press. 1932.

*New York Historical Society*. Ser. 2, vol. 1. 1841.

*Old South Leaflets*. Vol. 1, no. 17. (*Giovanni da Verrazzano's Voyage*). Boston, Direction of the Old South Work. 1889.

Parkman, Francis, *Pioneers of France in the New World*. Vol. 1. Boston, Little, Brown & Co. 1902.

Peixoto, Afranio, *Historia do Brasil*. Lisboa, Aillaud & Lello; Porto, Lello & Irmão. 1940.

Peragallo, Prospero, *Intorno alla supposta indentità di Giovanni da Verrazzano col corsaro francese Giovanni Florin*. (Memoria della Società Geografica Italiana. Vol. 7, pt. 1. Roma. 1897).

Peterson, Edward, *History of Rhode Island*. New York, J. S. Taylor. 1853.

Pimenta, Alfredo, *D. João III*. Porto, Livraria de Tavares Martins. 1936.

Pomba, Rocha, *Historia do Brasil*. São Paulo, Melhoramentos. 1961.

*Raccolta di Documenti e Studi*. Pt. 3, vol. 1, 1892; pt. 3, vol. 2, 1893; pt. 5, vol. 2, 1894. Pubblicati dalla Reale Commissione Colombiana. Roma. (Library files also list it as *Raccolta Colombiana*).

Ramusio, Giovanni Battista, *A la Découverte de l'Amérique du Nord. Navigations et Voyages XVI siècle*. (Translated from the Italian by Langlois and Simon). Paris, Centre de Documentation "André Thèvet." 1933.

Ramusio, Giovanni Battista, *Terzo volume de Navigationi e Viaggi* etc. Venetia, Lucantonio Giunti. 1556.

Santarem, Visconde Manuel Francisco Barrios de, *Quadro Elementar das Relações Politicas Diplomaticas de Portugal* etc. Vols. 2 and 3 (in one volume). Paris, J. P. Aillaud. 1842, 1843. (Library files also list the author's name under Barrios).

Savon, Marcos A., *Descubrimientos y Exploraciónes en la costa Sur Durante el Siglo XVI*. Vol. 3. Biblioteca del Oficial de Marina. 1929.

Smith, Buckingham, *An Inquiry into the Authenticity of Documents Concerning a Discovery in North America* etc. New York, J. F. Trow. 1864.

Smith, Marion J., *A History of Maine*. Portland, Falmouth Publishing House. 1949.

Sousa, Fr. Luis de, *Anais de D. João III*. 2 vols. Lisboa, Livraria Sa' Da Costa. 1938.

Sousa Viterbo, Francisco, *Trabalhos Nauticos Dos Portuguezes nos Seculos XVI e XVII*. 1898-1900. (Author also listed under Viterbo).

Southey, Robert, *History of Brazil*. Vol. 1. London, Longmans, Hurst, Rees, Orme and Brown. 1822.

Tanner, Earl C., *Rhode Island; a brief history*. Providence, Rhode Island State Board of Education etc. 1954.

*The Parkman Reader*. (Selected works edited by Samuel Eliot Morison). Boston, Little, Brown & Co. 1955.

Thèvet, André, *Les Singularitez de la France* etc. Paris, Chez de la Porte. 1558.

Tiraboschi, Girolamo, *Storia della Letteratura Italiana*. Vol. 3. Venezia, Antonio Rosa. 1803.

Turner, Henry E., *Settlers of Aquidneck*. Newport, Newport Historical Publishing Co. 1880.

Tytler, Patrick F., *Historical View of the Progress of Discovery on the More Northern Coasts of America*. Edinburgh, Oliver & Boyd; London, Simpkin & Marshall. 1832.

U. S. *Catholic Historical Society*. Pt. 1, vol. 3. 1903. (*The Globe of Ulpius and its Relation to the voyage of Verrazzano* etc. B. F. De Costa).

Varnhagen, Francisco A. de, *Historia Geral do Brasil*. Vols. 1 and 2. São Paulo, Melhoramentos. 1962.

Varnhagen, Francisco A. de, *Le Premier Voyage de Amerigo Vespucci*. Vienna, Gerold. 1869.

*Verrazzano's Voyage Along the Atlantic Coast of North America*. (New York State Local History Source Leaflets. Albany, University of the State of New York. 1916).

Vianna, Helio, *Historia do Brasil*. Vol. 1. São Paulo, Melhoramentos. 1961.

Vitet, Ludovie, *Histoire de Dieppe*. Paris, Bethune & Plon. 1844.

Weiser, Francis X., *The Holyday Book*. New York, Harcourt, Brace & World. 1965.

Wieder, Fredrick C. & Stokes, I. N. P., *The Iconography of Manhattan Island. 1498-1909*. New York, R. H. Dodd. 1915.

Winsor, Justin, *Narrative and Critical History of America*. Vols. 1-5. Boston & New York, Houghton, Mifflin Co. 1884, 1885.